D1093680

Flux Linkages and
Electromagnetic Induction

THE MACMILLAN COMPANY
NEW YORK · CHICAGO
DALLAS · ATLANTA · SAN FRANCISCO

MACMILLAN AND CO., LIMITED
LONDON · BOMBAY · CALCUTTA
MADRAS · MELBOURNE

**THE MACMILLAN COMPANY
OF CANADA, LIMITED**
TORONTO

Flux Linkages and Electromagnetic Induction

L. V. BEWLEY

*Professor and Director
of the Curriculum in
Electrical Engineering,
Lehigh University*

New York
THE MACMILLAN COMPANY

To my grandsons

ROBERT STEPHEN BEWLEY
RICHARD FRANK BEWLEY
JAMES THOMAS BEWLEY

PREFACE

As a young engineer just out of school and "on test" with the General Electric Company in the latter part of 1923, I was asked by the late R. E. Doherty, then a consulting engineer of the Company, to study and report on a certain patent proposal in which an ingenious method was revealed for the generation of direct current without the encumbrance of a commutator or a pair of slip rings for each conductor. I knew that this was supposed to be impossible, but I sweated for many an hour before I was able to put my finger on the fallacy in that patent application. Having done so, I laid myself open to a regular flood of similar propositions relayed to me with the blessings of the Patent Department. (It seems that the invention of means for the generation of direct current without a commutator is as intriguing to electrical engineers as the invention of perpetual motion is to mechanical engineers—and just about as profitable!) Finally, in self-defense, I was forced to look more deeply into this business of electromagnetic induction and to develop criteria which would show when, where, and what kind of a voltage would be induced in any given case. A number of years later I published a couple of papers and some discussions in the A.I.E.E. on the subject.*

* "Flux Linkages and Electromagnetic Induction in Closed Circuits" by L. V. Bewley, *Transactions A.I.E.E.*, vol. 48, April 1929, pp. 327–37.

"Induced Voltage of Electrical Machines" by L. V. Bewley, *Transactions A.I.E.E.*, vol. 49, April 1930, pp. 456–66.

"Discussion" by L. V. Bewley, *Transactions A.I.E.E.*, vol. 49, April 1930, pp. 453–54.

More recently, interest in the matter has erupted again*—it does so every few years, like a slumbering volcano!; this has induced me to prepare this small monograph on the subject, which I hope will help clarify the situation and show how ridiculously easy it is to understand and apply Faraday's law to any and all cases.

L. V. Bewley

---

* "Electromagnetic Induction" by G. I. Cohn, *Electrical Engineering*, vol. 68, May 1949, pp. 441–47.

"Letters to the Editor" in *Electrical Engineering* by Norton Savage, vol. 68, July 1949, p. 645; G. I. Cohn, vol. 68, Nov. 1949, p. 1018; L. V. Bewley, vol. 68, Dec. 1949, p. 1113; G. I. Cohn, vol. 69, Dec. 1950, p. 1138; L. V. Bewley, vol. 69, Dec. 1950, p. 1139.

CONTENTS

CHAPTER

    I Introduction   1

   II Circuits, Turns, and Flux Linkages   4

  III Substitution of Circuits   12

  IV Electromagnetic Induction   20

   V General Criteria for Electromagnetic Induction   39

  VI Applications and Paradoxes   44

 VII Theorem of Constant Flux Linkages   86

    Index   99

CHAPTER I

INTRODUCTION

The basic laws and underlying concepts of electromagnetic theory are few in number and beguilingly simple to state. The formula for any one of them may be written in a space the size of a postage stamp, Fig. 1. Out of these simple laws and concepts Maxwell constructed his great generalizations. By means of them a few generations of physicists and electrical engineers have developed an electrified age that has entered every nook and cranny of our modern civilization, with endless ramifications in the fields of power, transportation, communication, illumination, industry, agriculture, and domestic applications. There is, however, a vast gulf between the mere statement and elementary demonstration of these laws and concepts, and their successful application to specific cases of practical importance. The passage is often beset not only with many mathematical difficulties, but also by the fundamental problem of recognizing just what law, or perhaps what aspect of a given law, applies to the case at hand. And in this respect none of the basic laws or concepts has caused more uncertainty or led to greater misinterpretations—and so-called paradoxes—than the *Law of Electromagnetic Induction.* Faraday deduced experimentally the following rule:

> *Whenever the total net magnetic flux through a closed circuit varies there is induced in the circuit a voltage whose magnitude is proportional to the rate of diminution of the flux through the circuit.*

1

This law is universally true, whether either or both the magnetic system and the circuit are moving, and even if the circuit changes its configuration as well as position—so long as the circuit remains closed and unbroken. The flux density itself at any point may

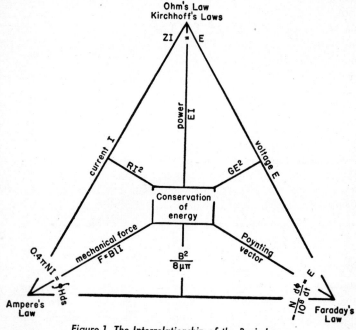

Figure 1. The Interrelationship of the Basic Laws.

change either because of a variation in the magnetomotive force which caused it, or a physical displacement of the magnetic system, or any other cause. The circuit need not be metallic or conducting. In fact it need be nothing more than an imaginary closed line in space, and the circuit may be as large or as small as we please.

Now the difficulties and misinterpretations which have been encountered in the application of Faraday's law appear to fall in three categories: (1) those cases in which the "total net magnetic flux" is not properly reckoned, (2) those cases in which "the rate of diminution of the flux through the circuit" is miscalculated, usually because several simultaneous effects mask each other, and (3) those cases in which a new circuit, or part of a circuit, is substituted for the original circuit by a breaking and mending operation. It is then the purpose of this monograph to investigate these points in some detail and so to formulate Faraday's law, along with suitable criteria, that there can exist no possibility of a misinterpretation of this fundamental law which is the principal foundation stone of electromagnetic theory and electrical engineering.

First of all, we shall consider the influence of the configuration of the circuit on the flux which links it, and this will introduce the concept and definition of a *turn*.

Next, we shall consider the matter of a *substitution of circuit*, whereby the flux linkages may be changed without inducing a voltage. We shall see that a failure to recognize a "substitution of circuit" is back of most of the misconceptions regarding Faraday's law. And yet it would be impossible to generate a d-c voltage without the agency of a substitution of circuit.

Then, we shall develop general equations for the voltage induced in a circuit and show how this voltage may be induced by either or both *transformer action* (because of the positional variation of the flux itself) and *cutting action* (because of the motion of the conductor through the flux). This development will necessarily entail an appeal to higher mathematics as the more general cases are considered.

Then, we shall formulate *general criteria* which will enable us to calculate properly the voltage induced in any circuit, and to determine with assurance the process by which the induction takes place.

Finally, we shall investigate a number of interesting cases in which it is not immediately clear what voltage will be induced and show that each of these so-called paradoxes reduces to a straightforward problem when subjected to an analysis based on the general criteria and a proper understanding of flux linkages and the processes of electromagnetic induction.

CHAPTER II

CIRCUITS, TURNS,
and FLUX LINKAGES

CIRCUITS

In order that no ambiguity shall exist as to the meaning of the
term *circuit*, as used in this book, the following definition will apply:

> *Any closed contour in space, whether in conducting
> media or not and disregarding whether parts
> thereof are common to any other selected contours,
> constitutes a closed circuit.*

On the basis of this definition, a network of n branches having
two or more junctions will have just as many separate and distinct
circuits as it is possible to trace closed paths in that network, even
though some of the branches are common to two or more of the
circuits. It is thus possible, for example, to construct a network of
$n(n-1)/2$ complete circuits with n flexible conductors if only
two junctions are used.

Associated with the concept of a circuit as a closed contour is
the idea of the *direction* in which this circuit is to be traced. In the
case of circuits which lie essentially in a plane, and which are not
twisted, it is customary to speak of the clockwise (c.w.) and
counterclockwise (c.c.w.) directions. But this is not sufficiently
clear; for what is c.w. to one observer is c.c.w. to another observer
on the opposite side, and in the case of twisted circuits the specification may be devoid of significance. For example, a person on one

4

side of a wheel will say that it is rotating c.w., while an observer on the other side will see it rotating c.c.w. Or take a simple circuit and twist it in the form of a figure 8; then as the circuit is traced, the direction is c.w. for one of the loops and c.c.w. for the other loop. Even in this simple case, one encounters the paradox of being able to leave a certain given starting point in, say, the c.w. direction only, whether he goes forward or backward! For suppose we take as the starting point on a circuit twisted in the form of a figure 8 a point on the top strand at the crossover. Then we can leave this point in the c.w. (or it may be the c.c.w., depending on the way the 8 is formed) direction only, and after completing the circuit we arrive back at the starting point by the c.c.w. direction.

In mathematics it is customary to designate the positive direction of a contour as that which keeps the surface enclosed by the contour to the left; but here again doubt arises as to how to consider a twisted circuit, such as a figure 8. Evidently, a more reliable method of designating direction is needed. We have already seen that the configuration of the circuit, the position of the observer, and the designation of the starting point, may be essential to a foolproof definition. There is no doubt that a definition of direction independent of an observer, or of any superimposed quantity (such as a flux line), would be most desirable, for then direction would be a concept associated with the structure of space itself. However, in practical applications, such a definition might very well prove to be too abstract.

If it is possible to construct a closed circuit of any configuration by the operations of folding, turning, twisting, and knotting (but the author does not assert that it is always possible), then the concept of direction may be tied to the plane single-loop circuit whose distortion by these various operations results in the actual configuration. Thus, referring to Fig. 2, there is shown a single-loop plane circuit C oriented with respect to a coordinate system (x,y,z), with an observer at point (x_0,y_0,z_0) and a specified starting point A (x_1,y_1,z_1) on the circuit. Now for this case direction may be defined in a variety of consistent ways. For example, positive direction is:

(1) the direction in which the interior area bounded by the circuit is kept on the left, or

(2) the direction c.c.w. with respect to the observer, or

(3) the direction in which a right-hand screw must be turned to advance toward the observer, or

(4) the direction from A to B.

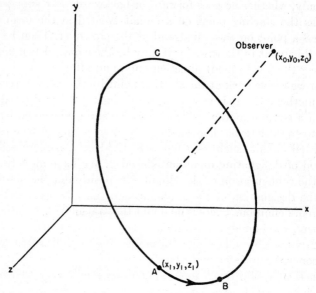

Figure 2. Direction of a Circuit.

Of these, the first may appear at first sight to be independent of the observer, but it is not so, for it tacitly assumes one side of the circuit to be the "top" side. The starting point, (x_1,y_1,z_1), is not a necessary part of the definition in this case.

Now suppose our simple, single-loop plane circuit is subjected to the distortions indicated in Fig. 3. In all cases we shall consider the starting point A to be "nailed down," and the observer to be "looking down" and far enough removed to see the assorted circuits in their entirety.

Figure 3(a) shows a single-loop circuit in the plane of the paper, with a starting point A an adjacent point B and the c.c.w. direction (with respect to the observer) chosen as positive.

Figure 3(b) shows the original circuit, Fig. 3(a), simply turned over. With respect to the observer the positive direction (from A to B) is now c.w., and the encircled area is on the right instead of on the left.

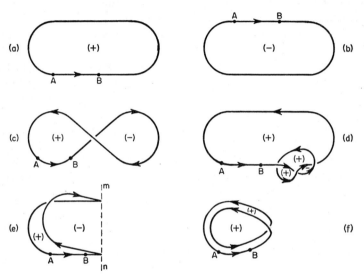

Figure 3. The Twisting, Turning, Folding and Knotting of a Circuit.

Figure 3(c) shows the circuit twisted into a figure 8. With respect to the observer, one loop is c.c.w. and the other c.w., and the encircled areas are respectively positive and negative.

Figure 3(d) shows a knot in the circuit. This knot cannot be made in the original circuit, Fig. 3(a), without first cutting that circuit, and then mending it after the knot is inserted. From the point of view of the observer, some parts of the knot may be positive and others negative, depending on whether they tend to encircle a ray from the observer in the c.c.w. or c.w. direction.

Figure 3(e) shows the original circuit, Fig. 3(a), folded back on itself. The observer could consider this to constitute two loops, with respect to an imaginary line *mn*, one positive and one negative.

Figure 3(f) shows the twisted circuit, Fig. 3(c), folded over on itself. The twist resulted in a negative loop, but the folding converted this loop back into a positive loop.

These sketches illustrate the possibility of constructing complicated circuits by suitable distortion—twisting, folding, turning, knotting, etc.—of a simple plane loop. However, even if this is always possible, the converse operation, that of unraveling a tortuous circuit, may defy our best efforts, and yet we must have some means of determining what is the positive direction in an electric circuit. So whatever interest these digressions may have from the point of view of topology, we must abandon them in favor of a more simple proposition. Fortunately, in electromagnetic induction problems, our concern over a circuit direction is always with reference to the direction of the flux enclosed by the circuit; and in a sense the direction of a tube of flux takes the place of an observer. Figure 4(a) shows a simple, single-loop circuit enclosing, or linked with, a line of flux, ϕ.

> *Positive circuit direction is taken, arbitrarily, as*
> *the direction of rotation of a right-hand screw as it*
> *advances in the positive direction of the flux.*

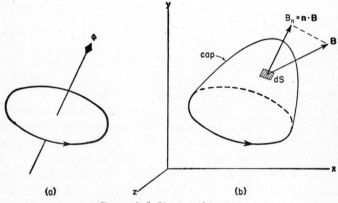

Figure 4. A Circuit and Its Cap.

In order to calculate the total flux through the circuit, we imagine a surface, or cap, of which the circuit is the boundary, Fig. 4(b), and consider the normal component of flux density $B_n(x,y,z,t)$ at any point on this surface. In general, B_n is a function of the point (x,y,z) as well as of time t, for it may be varying in any arbitrary manner. The instantaneous value of the total flux through the surface—and therefore through the boundary circuit—is

$$\phi = \iint B_n \, dS \tag{1}$$

in which dS is the area of an element of the surface where the normal component of flux density is B_n and the integral is to be taken over the entire surface of which the circuit is the boundary.

Now in subsequent derivations it is convenient to express Eq. (1) in vector analysis notation. To that end let

n = unit vector of the outward normal to the surface dS
B = $iB_x + jB_y + kB_z$ = flux density at dS
B_n = $n \cdot B$ = component of flux density normal to dS

Then (1) may be written

$$\phi = \iint B_n \, dS = \iint n \cdot B \, dS \tag{2}$$

It is to be noted that no restrictions are made as to the shape of the cap. It is conceivable that it may contain wrinkles or convolutions, so that a given line of flux may pierce it at several points. In such a case the angle between n, the unit normal to the surface and the positive flux density vector B is greater than $\pi/2$; so that the dot product $n \cdot B$ is negative where the flux enters the cap and positive where it emerges from the cap, and the integral, Eq. (2), gives the net flux emerging from the cap, or linked with the circuit.

Now it may happen that the circuit overlaps itself a number of times in such a way that the supported surface may be subdivided into several subsurfaces, each of which is pierced by the same flux lines. Such a circuit is said to be a multiple-turn circuit. How is this subdivision to be accomplished? Figure 5 shows such a circuit in which the same flux ϕ is obviously linked several times with the encircling circuit. In order to count the encirclements we may connect points *a,c,e,g* by dotted lines and observe that *abc, cde, efg,* and *gha* each represents one complete circuit or turn. On each of these circuits we can place a cap or membrane and by integrating the normal components of flux density over these surfaces arrive at the total flux linked with the complete circuit.

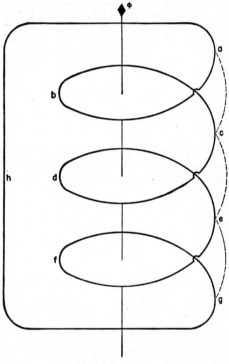

Figure 5. Turns.

There is another possibility. Suppose in Fig. 5 that the roles of the circuit and of the flux are interchanged, so that *a-b-c* · · · *h-a* becomes the line of flux and ϕ is part of a circuit closing to the right. The "flux linkages" are the same as in the previous case. We conclude that it is immaterial whether the "turns" are in the circuit or in the flux path.

We are now able to formulate a definition for a *turn*. A turn is so intuitively self-evident in most cases of engineering practice as to require no explanation, but when tubes of induction are interwound with a circuit there is some chance for confusion. The following arbitrary definition will therefore be adopted for the purpose of this book.

> *If it is possible by means of imaginary lines to subdivide a circuit into a network of N cells such that each cell encloses the same flux ϕ and in the same direction, then the circuit is said to have N turns with respect to ϕ.*

On the basis of the above definition, the actual physical loops may be made by either the circuit or by the tubes of induction, and the specification of the number of turns present is entirely arbitrary. In any particular case the induced voltage may be computed on the basis of N circuits in series each linked with a flux ϕ, or of a single turn circuit linked with a flux $N\phi$. To prove the equivalence it is only necessary to note that the voltage round any circuit C which has been so subdivided into N cells $1, 2, 3 \cdots N$, is equal to the sum of the voltages round each cell, all taken in the same direction, thus

$$E_c = E_1 + E_2 + \cdots + E_N$$

CHAPTER III

SUBSTITUTION OF CIRCUITS

The majority of the so-called paradoxes in electromagnetic induction are merely cases in which a change in flux linkages have been brought about by substituting one circuit, or part of a circuit, for another, and erroneously charging this change in flux linkages to Faraday's law. We call this a *substitution of circuit*. Familiar examples are sliding contacts, switching, commutation, winding on of turns, and amputation. A substitution of circuit cannot of itself result in voltage induction, although it may cause a change in magnetomotive force which in turn will cause the flux itself to change. But it is important to understand that any voltage which may be induced owes its origin to a change in the flux itself and not to the substitution of circuit. In many of the paradoxes there is an apparent change of flux linkages which bears no relationship to the voltage induced, because part of the change is due to a varying flux and part due to a substitution of circuit. The two effects mask each other and lead to confusion, unless there is a clear understanding of the processes involved. This matter is of such importance as to justify a statement in the form of a definition and law:

> *A substitution of circuit is the replacement of one circuit, or part of a circuit, by another circuit, and cannot, of itself, induce a voltage.*

Substitutions of circuit are of great practical importance, for without them, as we shall see, it is impossible to generate direct current by electrical machines.

Every substitution of circuit involves the breaking and making of circuits, usually in a repetitious fashion, and therefore some sort of switching operation or sliding contact is required. But every sliding contact does not result in a substitution of circuit. A sliding contact which is merely a mechanical convenience inserted for the purpose of connecting, say, a moving part of a circuit to a stationary part of the same circuit, does not necessarily involve a substitution of circuit.

THE SLIDING CONTACT

Figure 6(a) shows the cross section of a laminated magnetic core M having five laminations numbered 1, 2, 3, 4, 5. The laminations are insulated from each other. An external circuit abc having sliding contacts a and b is moving along the sides of the core, and at the instant shown the circuit is completed from a to b through lamination 2, as indicated by the dash line. An instant later the circuit will have moved to the left and the sliding contacts a and b will then be on lamination 3. A substitution of circuit has occurred, for the circuit $a3bca$ is a *different* circuit than $a2bca$. The situation is no different than that shown in Fig. 6(b) in which the circuits through the laminations are completed by switches s_1, s_2, s_3, s_4, s_5. Switch s_2 is shown closed. If s_2 is opened and s_3 is closed, a new circuit will be substituted for the old one.

Obviously, the flux linkages are different for circuit $a3bca$ than for circuit $a2bca$, by the amount of flux in one lamination. But no voltage has been induced by the sliding contacts, any more than the opening and closing of the switches in Fig. 6(b) would induce a voltage.

The laminations were included merely for the purpose of emphasizing that new circuits are being substituted as the sliding contact moves from position to position. But the same thing occurs if there are no laminations as indicated in Fig. 6(c), for the current paths—

and therefore the circuits—are different when the contacts are in position *ab* than for position *a'b'*.

Figure 6(d) shows the magnetic core *M* flanked by heavy copper conductors *pq*, and the sliding contacts *a* and *b* move along the surface of these conductors. Now the current paths through the

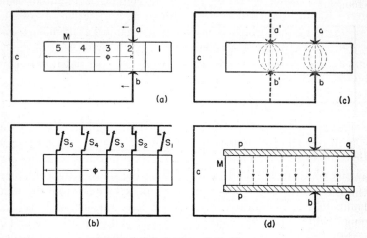

Figure 6. Substitutions of Circuit.

core itself are independent of the position of the sliding contacts and any one of the circuits is the same for all positions of the contacts. This is a case, then, in which the sliding contacts are simply a mechanical convenience for connecting the stationary and moving parts of the circuit. The slip rings of an alternator serve exactly the same purpose. There is no substitution of circuit with respect to the flux, for each of the multiple circuits links the same flux regardless of the position of the contacts. Therefore,

> *A sliding contact which does not result in a change of flux linkages is not a substitution of circuit.*

In the examples of Fig. 6 the moving elements of the circuit are *external* to the flux in the core *M*, and, as a result of the movement, either the part of the circuit completed through the flux is undergoing a substitution of circuit, Fig. 6(a), (b), (c), or else remains unchanged, Fig. 6(d). Now suppose that the moving part of the circuit cuts through the flux, as in Fig. 7(a). In this case, as the sliding contacts *ab* move to position *a'b'*, the flux linkages change by $\Delta\phi$. Has a substitution of circuit occurred? No, because the change in flux linkages is due entirely to the cutting action alone,

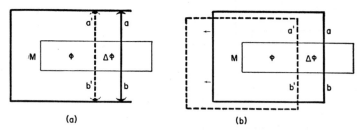

(a)   (b)

Figure 7. A Sliding Contact Which Does Not Result in a Substitution of Circuit.

and the sliding contact plays no essential part in bringing about this change $\Delta\phi$. In fact, if the whole external circuit is moved bodily, as in Fig. 7(b), the same change of flux linkages, $\Delta\phi$, occurs. This is another case in which the sliding contacts are not of themselves responsible for a change of flux linkages, but serve merely as a moving connection.

WINDING ON OF TURNS

A substitution of circuit can be accomplished by winding turns around a magnetic core, as shown in Fig. 8. Here a core *M* of flux ϕ has a drum *d* with *N* turns about one leg. This drum has a slip ring *a* on which bears a brush *b* connecting to the external circuit *c*. If the drum is revolved, the number of turns will increase, thereby increasing the flux linkages. At any one instant the flux linkages are $N\phi$, in which ϕ is a constant and N a variable. No voltage is induced by this process. If slip ring *a* is complete, there are actually two circuits in parallel in this arrangement, and the number of turns N is always an integer, changing abruptly by one every time the connection to the slip ring passes under the brush. To see this refer to Fig. 9. In Fig. 9(a) the tap *a* is shown under the brush, and starting at *b* three turns 1, 2, 3 are seen to surround the core. Now let the drum be revolved, say one-third of a revolution in the c.w. direction, as shown in Fig. 9(b). Starting at brush *b* we can trace one c.w. path *b x a 1 2 3* of *three* turns, and another path *b y a 1 2 3*,

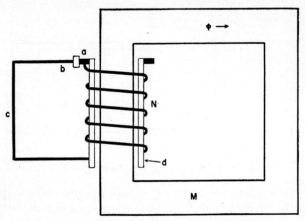

Figure 8. Substitution of Circuit by Winding on of Turns.

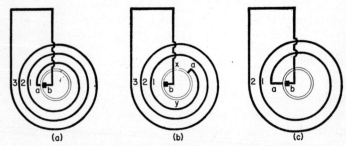

Figure 9. Substitution of Circuit by Winding on of Turns.

partly c.c.w. and partly c.w., of *two* turns. Finally, after a complete c.w. revolution, Fig. 9(c), the number of turns has reduced to $N = 2$ by either path.

> *The number of turns is always an integer, and if the number varies, the change is made abruptly by one*

turn. In a drum and slip ring arrangement there are always two paths in parallel through the slip ring, and the number of turns of one of the paths is one less than that of the other path; except at the instant when the slip ring tap passes under the brush, at which instant the turns of one of the paths change to equality with that of the other path.

Of course, one of the paths can be eliminated by cutting the slip ring axially at one point.

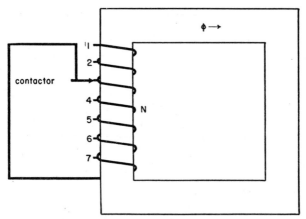

Figure 10. Substitution of Circuit by Tap Changing.

Another way in which the number of turns interlinked with a flux may be changed is shown by the scheme of Fig. 10, in which a contactor simply shifts from tap to tap on a winding (just as in a transformer with taps). In this scheme again the turns change abruptly at each shift, although there is no reason why each shift cannot involve any number of turns.

If we take the number of turns to be a function of time, then since the number is always an integer and changes abruptly, the time function must be a staircase function as shown in Fig. 11 for decreasing turns. The derivative is discontinuous.

$$\frac{dN}{dt} = \begin{cases} 0 & \text{for } t_k < t < t_{k+1} \\ \pm \infty & t = t_k \end{cases}$$

The flux linkages are $N\phi$, and we have seen that changing these $\pm \phi$ by adding or subtracting a turn does not induce a voltage. We may write the induced voltage for this case as

$$e = \phi \frac{dN}{dt} = 0 \tag{3}$$

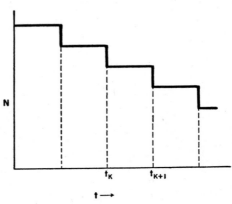

Figure 11.

A substitution of circuit by means of a sliding contact is, in a sense, a double change in N, for when one circuit is disconnected the turns interlinked with the flux are reduced to zero, and when the new circuit is substituted, the turns establish new flux linkages. .

COMMUTATION

The commutator of a motor or generator is a device for effecting a continual substitution of circuit, and as we shall see in a subsequent chapter, a substitution of circuit (usually by means of a commutator) is a necessary process in the generation of a d-c voltage.

Figure 12 shows a Gramme ring armature with brushes a and b bearing on the commutator. There are two circuits in parallel at

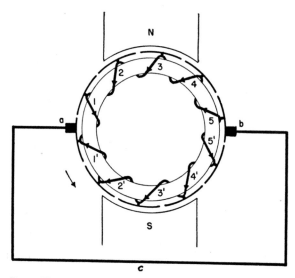

Figure 12. Substitution of Circuit by Means of a Commutator.

any one instant: the circuit *a12345bca* and the circuit *a1'2'3'4'5'bca*. The directions of the induced voltage are opposite in the upper and lower parts of the armature. Now if the armature revolves one commutator segment, coil *1* will be transferred to the lower circuit while coil *5'* will be transferred to the upper circuit, and the voltages induced in these coils by rotation through the field flux will be reversed. Thus coils *1* and *5'* have been taken out of one circuit and inserted in another circuit—a substitution of circuit has taken place.

CHAPTER IV

ELECTROMAGNETIC INDUCTION

RATE OF CHANGE OF FLUX LINKAGES

In the previous chapters we have considered in some detail the meaning of the terms circuit, turns, substitution of circuit, and flux linkages. We must now examine the ways in which the flux linkages can be varied and the conditions under which the change will induce a voltage.

If a circuit consists of N turns linked with a flux ϕ, then the flux linkages are

$$\Omega = N\phi \tag{4}$$

Regarding both N and ϕ as functions of time, the rate of change of flux linkages is

$$\frac{d\Omega}{dt} = N\frac{d\phi}{dt} + \phi\frac{dN}{dt} \tag{5}$$

The term $N\,d\phi/dt$ of Eq. (5) accounts for those changes in interlinkages which are caused by varying the flux through the circuit. It expresses Faraday's Law of Electromagnetic Induction:

> *Whenever the total flux through a circuit varies there is an electromotive force induced whose magnitude is proportional to the rate of diminution of the total number of tubes of induction threading the circuit.*

It is important to note that the circuit under consideration remains intact under this interpretation and that it is the interlinked flux which changes. It will be shown in the next article that this flux may be varied in different ways, leading to such concepts as "transformer action" and "cutting action," but for the present it is sufficient to observe that $d\phi/dt$ must be other than zero, that is, ϕ must vary, if a voltage is induced.

The term $\phi\, dN/dt$ in Eq. (5) accounts for those changes in interlinkages which are caused by changing the number of turns linked with a given rigid distribution of flux. We saw in the previous chapter that if the number of turns is a function of time, $N(t)$, that N can only change instantaneously by a discrete integer number of turns, and at the instant of change dN/dt is always infinite. Thus the flux linkages can be changed suddenly by the substitution of circuit represented here by dN/dt. However, *no voltage is induced in the circuit* by this operation.

Thus it is possible to change the flux linkages in two fundamentally different ways: (1) by changing the flux and inducing a voltage and (2) by changing the circuit without inducing a voltage. We are therefore confronted with the possibility of building up the flux linkages by one process and of reducing them by the other process so as to induce a d-c voltage without permitting the flux ever to exceed a finite value. The induced voltage is always

$$e = -N\frac{d\phi}{dt} \tag{6}$$

THE AVERAGE OR D-C COMPONENT OF VOLTAGE

The average voltage induced in a non-interrupted circuit over the time interval $(t_2 - t_1)$ is, from Eq. (6)

$$e_{\mathrm{av}} = -\frac{N}{t_2 - t_1}\int_{t_1}^{t_2}\frac{d\phi}{dt}\,dt = -\frac{N}{t_2 - t_1}(\phi_2 - \phi_1) \tag{7}$$

in which ϕ_1 and ϕ_2 are the values of the flux at t_1 and t_2 respectively. It is evident that $e_{\mathrm{av}}\to 0$ if averaged over a sufficiently long period of time, for the flux ϕ_2 cannot increase perpetually. At first glance this would seem to preclude the possibility of inducing a constant or d-c voltage.

Suppose, however, that at time t_2, when the flux included by the circuit is ϕ_2, the interlinkages to be reduced to the starting value $N\phi_1$, by effecting a substitution of circuit, $\phi\,dN/dt$; and

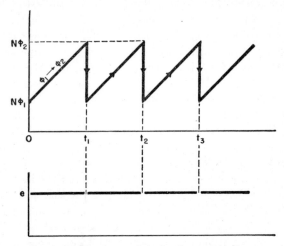

Figure 13. The Generation of a Constant Voltage.

then that the flux linkage of the new or substituted circuit be increased linearly by increasing the flux, $N\,d\phi/dt$. No voltage will be induced by the substitution of circuit and a constant voltage will be induced by the linear rate of change of flux. Any number of such cycles may be passed through in succession and the average voltage induced over all the cycles is

$$e_{\text{av}} = -\frac{\Sigma\,N\,(\phi_k - \phi_{k-1})}{\Sigma\,(t_k - t_{k-1})} \tag{8}$$

If every substituted circuit and cycle is alike, this becomes

$$e_{\text{av}} = -N\frac{\phi_2 - \phi_1}{t_2 - t_1} \tag{9}$$

The sequence of events is depicted in Fig. 13. The flux increases linearly from ϕ_1 to ϕ_2, with N constant, in the interval $t_2 - t_1$, inducing a constant voltage e. At instants t_1, t_2, t_3, $\cdots$ the flux linkages are reduced from $N\phi_2$ back to $N\phi_1$ by a substitution of circuit.

Thus a d-c component of voltage may be obtained over any period of time, merely by providing some arrangement whereby new circuits are continually substituted for old circuits as the limit in flux linkages is reached for each. And therefore, in any d-c generator the voltage must be induced by a change of flux $N\,d\phi/dt$, but the interlinkages held within finite bounds by a periodic reduction $\phi\,dN/dt$.

The most familiar arrangement of this kind is the ordinary d-c generator, wherein a commutator functions as an automatic switch connecting the armature coils to the external circuit. At regular intervals each armature coil is disconnected from the external circuit, on being short-circuited by the brushes, and is then immediately substituted back into the circuit, but with reversed connection.

Other methods of generating a d-c voltage will be discussed in Chapter V.

VOLTAGE INDUCTION IN A SIMPLE CASE

Before proceeding to the general case of voltage induction in a completely flexible coil of any instantaneous configuration moving in any way and at any velocity in a variable field of flux, it is advisable to consider some simpler case which nevertheless will exhibit the same basic phenomena of induction.

Figure 14 illustrates a concentrated and rigid rectangular coil of N turns and length l in a direction perpendicular to the plane of the paper (the z-axis). The coil is assumed to be moving along the x-axis at any velocity through a magnetic field whose density, perpendicular to the plane of the coil, is $B(x,t)$, hence a function of both the coordinate x and time t.

The flux linked with the coil in the xz-plane, having parallel coil sides along the z-axis, is

$$\phi = \int_0^{x_2}\!\!\int_{x_1} B(x,t)dx\,dz = l\int_{x_1}^{x_2} B(x,t)\,dx \tag{10}$$

But if the coil is moving, the positions x_1 and x_2 of the coil sides are functions of time t. Therefore, in taking the derivative of ϕ to determine the induced voltage in accordance with Eq. (6), we must

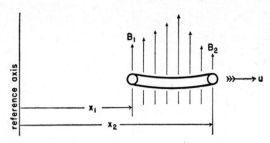

Figure 14. Rigid Coil Moving through a Varying Magnetic Field.

use the rule pertaining to the differentiation of a definite integral whose limits, as well as integrand, are functions of the parameter (in this case t) with respect to which differentiation is performed. Thus

$$e = -N\frac{d\phi}{dt} = -Nl\,\frac{d}{dt}\int_{x_1(t)}^{x_2(t)} B(x,t)\,dx$$

$$= -Nl\left(\int_{x_1}^{x_2} \frac{\partial B(x,t)}{\partial t}\,dx + B(x_2,t)\,\frac{dx_2}{dt} - B(x_1,t)\,\frac{dx_1}{dt}\right) \quad (11)$$

But

$$-Nl\int_{x_1}^{x_2} \frac{\partial B(x,t)}{\partial t}\,dx = -N\frac{\partial}{\partial t}l\int_{x_1}^{x_2} B(x,t)\,dx = -N\frac{\partial\phi(x_2,x_1,t)}{\partial t} \quad (12)$$

in which the partial derivative clearly indicates that the variables x_2 and x_1 are to be taken as constant while the partial derivative with respect to t is taken; in other words, the motion of the coil is not considered—only its instantaneous position. The flux between fixed points x_1 and x_2 is varying as a function of time and inducing a voltage given by Eq. (12). This is called the *variational component of induced voltage*, or simply "transformer action," since it is the recognized process of voltage induction in a transformer.

Now the terms dx_2/dt and dx_1/dt in Eq. (11) are obviously the velocities of the moving coil sides in the x-direction, or u_2 and u_1 respectively. Then the corresponding terms in Eq. (11) become

$$\left. \begin{aligned} -NlB(x_2,t)\,\frac{dx_2}{dt} &= -NlB_2u_2 \\ -NlB(x_1,t)\,\frac{dx_1}{dt} &= -NlB_1u_1 \end{aligned} \right\} \tag{13}$$

and if the coil is rigid $u_1 = u_2 = u$. Thus those terms in Eq. (11) give an induced voltage

$$-Nl(B_2 - B_1)u \tag{14}$$

which is the familiar *Blv* rule of elementary electrical engineering. Equation (14) prescribes the possibility of inducing a voltage by movement of the coil through the flux densities B_2 and B_1 at the coil side locations x_2 and x_1 respectively. This is called the *motional component of induced voltage*, or simply "cutting action." It is the recognized process of voltage induction in a d-c generator, in which the conductors cut through the constant flux density of the field poles. The physical interpretation of Eq. (13) or (14) is obvious: lu is the area swept out per unit time by the moving coil side, and this area multiplied by the flux density gives the total flux moved through by the coil side per unit time.

By Eqs. (12) and (13) or (14) in (11) we have for the total induced voltage

$$e = -N\left(\frac{\partial\phi}{\partial t} + lB_2u_2 - lB_1u_1\right)$$

$$= \underbrace{-N\,\frac{\partial\phi}{\partial t}}_{\substack{\text{transformer}\\\text{action}}} - \underbrace{Nl(B_2 - B_1)u}_{\substack{\text{cutting}\\\text{action}}} \tag{15}$$

This same equation may be established quite simply by noting from Fig. 14 that the flux linked with the coil is a function of x_2, x_1, and t, thus

$$\phi = \phi(x_2, x_1, t) \qquad (16)$$

Then differentiating Eq. (16) as a function of three variables

$$e = -N \frac{d\phi}{dt} = -N\left(\frac{\partial\phi}{\partial t}\frac{dt}{dt} + \frac{\partial\phi}{\partial x_2}\frac{dx_2}{dt} + \frac{\partial\phi}{\partial x_1}\frac{dx_1}{dt}\right)$$

$$= -N\left(\frac{\partial\phi}{\partial t} + lB_2 u_2 - lB_1 u_1\right)$$

$$= -N\frac{\partial\phi}{\partial t} - Nl(B_2 - B_1)u \quad \text{for a rigid coil} \qquad (17)$$

since the increment of flux added by the advance of the leading coil side is $d\phi = lB_2\, dx_2$ while the increment of flux added by the advance of the trailing coil side is $d\phi = -lB_1\, dx_1$.

It is worth while to take note of some implications in Eq. (15) or (17):

(1) A coordinate system is specified and all flux densities and movements explicitly referred to this coordinate system (in this case, the x- and z-axes and their origin).

(2) The rectangular coil of N turns is never broken, although it may be allowed to stretch if the two coil sides have different velocities u_2 and u_1.

(3) The variational, or transformer, component of the induced voltage, represented by $-N\,\partial\phi/\partial t$, is independent of the motion or velocity of the coil and depends only on the rate of change in space of the flux included within the coil. It is calculated at any instant on the assumption that the coil is stationary at that instant and that only the flux varies.

(4) The motional, or cutting, component of the induced voltage, represented by $-Nl(B_2 - B_1)u$, is independent of the space variation of the flux and depends only on the instantaneous flux densities at, and velocities of, the coil sides. It is calculated at

any instant on the assumption that the flux density and velocities are constant at that instant.

(5) There is no relationship between either the magnitudes or signs of the two components of induced voltage, and they may be in any proportion. It may be possible for one component to nullify completely the other component.

(6) The presence, magnitudes, and signs of the two components depend essentially on the selection of the coordinate system. The reference axis may be stationary in space, fixed to the moving coil, or moving in either direction at any velocity. Obviously, if the reference axis is fixed to the coil, there can be no velocity u of the coil with respect thereto, and any voltage induced must be due entirely to the variational component $N\,\partial\phi/\partial t$. On the other hand, for a reference axis fixed to a constant distribution of flux density, say a rotating field, the variation of flux with respect to the reference axis, $\partial\phi/\partial t$, is zero, and any voltage induced must be due entirely to the motional component $N(B_2 - B_1)\,ul$.

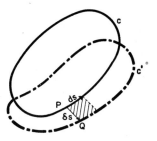

Figure 15. Coil Moving and Changing Shape in a Varying Magnetic Field.

THE GENERAL SOLUTION

There are several ways of obtaining the general solution for the case of electromagnetic induction in a flexible circuit of any shape, moving at any velocity, through a variable magnetic field, but these solutions depend on advanced mathematical concepts. We shall obtain the solution by two different methods, but will be obliged to use vector analysis and the calculus of variations.

Consider a flexible circuit C, Fig. 15, situated in a field of variable magnetic flux density

$$B = i\alpha + j\beta + k\gamma \tag{18}$$

in which (α,β,γ) are the x,y,z-components of the flux density, and

(i, j, k) are the unit vectors in the x,y,z-directions, respectively. The flux density components are assumed to be functions of time t. Now B is a solenoidal vector whose divergence is zero, that is,

$$\nabla \cdot B = \frac{\partial \alpha}{\partial x} + \frac{\partial \beta}{\partial y} + \frac{\partial \gamma}{\partial z} = 0 \tag{19}$$

Maxwell defined the vector potential

$$A = iX + jY + kZ \tag{20}$$

by the relationships

$$\left. \begin{aligned} \nabla \times A &= B \\ \nabla \cdot A &= 0 \end{aligned} \right\} \tag{21}$$

or written out

$$i\left(\frac{\partial Z}{\partial y} - \frac{\partial Y}{\partial z}\right) + j\left(\frac{\partial X}{\partial z} - \frac{\partial Z}{\partial x}\right) + k\left(\frac{\partial Y}{\partial x} - \frac{\partial X}{\partial y}\right) =$$
$$i\alpha + j\beta + k\gamma \tag{22}$$

$$\frac{\partial X}{\partial x} + \frac{\partial Y}{\partial y} + \frac{\partial Z}{\partial z} = 0 \tag{23}$$

It follows from Stokes' theorem that the flux linked with circuit C is

$$\phi = \iint n \cdot B \, dS = \iint n \cdot \nabla \times A \, dS = \oint A \cdot ds = L \tag{24}$$

in which n is the unit normal to any surface S of which C is the boundary contour, ds is an element on that contour, and L is the line integral.

Now as the circuit moves and changes its shape from C to C', the flux linked therewith also changes; so that in general the flux included by the circuit is a function of the shape and position of the circuit as well as of time t. But the shape and position of the circuit, with respect to the magnetic field, are sufficiently characterized by the line integral L as given in Eq. (24) if we take A as constant with respect to t. Therefore, functionally

$$\phi = \phi(t,L) \tag{25}$$

Now suppose the circuit to move and change its shape in such a manner that point P of the circuit moves to an adjacent point Q a differential distance δs away. This is the "variation" of the calculus of variations, and is to be distinguished from an element ds of the circuit itself. Then from (25)

$$\delta\phi = \frac{\partial\phi}{\partial t}\,\delta t + \frac{\partial\phi}{\partial L}\,\delta L = \frac{\partial\phi}{\partial t}\,\delta t + \delta L \tag{26}$$

since $\phi = L$ at any given instant and therefore

$$\frac{\partial\phi}{\partial L} = 1$$

Now

$$ds = \boldsymbol{i}\,dx + \boldsymbol{j}\,dy + \boldsymbol{k}\,dz \tag{27}$$

and therefore

$$\begin{aligned}
\delta L = \delta \oint \boldsymbol{A} \cdot d\boldsymbol{s} &= \delta \oint (X\,dx + Y\,dy + Z\,dz) \\
&= \oint \delta (X\,dx + Y\,dy + Z\,dz) \\
&= \oint (\delta X\,dx + X\delta\,dx + \text{similar terms in } Y \text{ and } Z) \\
&= \oint (\delta X\,dx + X d\,\delta x + \text{similar terms in } Y \text{ and } Z)
\end{aligned} \tag{28}$$

where, in accordance with the Calculus of Variations, we have put $d\,\delta x = \delta\,dx$.

Integrating by parts

$$\oint X d\,\delta x = X\,\delta x]_c - \oint \delta x\,dX = -\oint \delta x\,dX \tag{29}$$

since at the start and finish of a completed contour $X\,\delta x$ has the same value. Also

$$\delta X = \frac{\partial X}{\partial x}\,\delta x + \frac{\partial X}{\partial y}\,\delta y + \frac{\partial X}{\partial z}\,\delta z \tag{30}$$

and

$$dX = \frac{\partial X}{\partial x}\,dx + \frac{\partial X}{\partial y}\,dy + \frac{\partial X}{\partial z}\,dz \tag{31}$$

Hence by Eqs. (29), (30), and (31) in (28) we have

$$\delta L = \oint \left(\frac{\partial X}{\partial x} \delta x \, dx + \frac{\partial X}{\partial y} \delta y \, dx + \frac{\partial X}{\partial z} \delta z \, dx \right.$$

$$- \frac{\partial X}{\partial x} \delta x \, dx - \frac{\partial X}{\partial y} \delta x \, dy - \frac{\partial X}{\partial z} \delta x \, dz$$

$$\left. + \text{ similar terms in } Y \text{ and } Z \right) \tag{32}$$

Collecting terms and rearranging,

$$\delta L = \oint \left[\left(\frac{\partial Z}{\partial y} - \frac{\partial Y}{\partial z} \right) (dz \, \delta y - dy \, \delta z) \right.$$

$$+ \left(\frac{\partial X}{\partial z} - \frac{\partial Z}{\partial x} \right) (dx \, \delta z - dz \, \delta x)$$

$$\left. + \left(\frac{\partial Y}{\partial x} - \frac{\partial X}{\partial y} \right) (dy \, \delta x - dx \, \delta y) \right] \tag{33}$$

But the terms involving X, Y, Z will be recognized as the components of the curl of A, and the terms involving the differentials and variations as the components of the cross product of the vectors δs and ds. Therefore, by (21), (33) becomes

$$\delta L = \oint (\nabla \times A) \cdot (\delta s \times ds) = \oint B \cdot (\delta s \times ds) \tag{34}$$

in which

$$\delta s = i \, \delta x + j \, \delta y + k \, \delta z \tag{35}$$

is the displacement of a point on C.

Substituting Eq. (34) in (26)

$$\delta \phi = \frac{\partial \phi}{\partial t} \delta t + \oint B \cdot \delta s \times ds \tag{36}$$

or dividing through by δt gives for the induced voltage

$$e = -\frac{\delta\phi}{\delta t} = -\left(\frac{\partial\phi}{\partial t} + \oint \boldsymbol{B} \cdot \frac{\delta\boldsymbol{s}}{\delta t} \times d\boldsymbol{s}\right) \qquad (37)$$

But

$$\frac{\delta\boldsymbol{s}}{\delta t} = \boldsymbol{i}\frac{\delta x}{\delta t} + \boldsymbol{j}\frac{\delta y}{\delta t} + \boldsymbol{k}\frac{\delta z}{\delta t} = \boldsymbol{i}u + \boldsymbol{j}v + \boldsymbol{k}w = \boldsymbol{V} \qquad (38)$$

is the vector velocity of a point on C. Therefore,

$$e = -\left(\frac{\partial\phi}{\partial t} + \oint \boldsymbol{B} \cdot \boldsymbol{V} \times d\boldsymbol{s}\right) = -\left(\frac{\partial\phi}{\partial t} + \oint B_n V \sin\theta \, ds\right) \qquad (39)$$

where θ is the angle between $\boldsymbol{V}$ and $d\boldsymbol{s}$, and B_n is the component of $\boldsymbol{B}$ normal to the plane of $\boldsymbol{V}$ and $d\boldsymbol{s}$.

This general equation of the Law of Induction states that the electromotive force induced in a closed circuit is equal to the negative of:

> *The time rate of change in magnitude of that flux in space which is linked at the given instant with the circuit*
>
> *plus*
>
> *the sum for all the elements around the circuit of the triple product (length of the moving element of circuit)* × *(component of velocity perpendicular to the length of the element)* × *(component of flux density normal to the plane of motion of the element).*

The first part of this law gives the *variational* or *transformer action* component of the induced voltage. The second part gives the *motional* or *cutting action component* of the induced voltage. In general, the relative magnitudes of these two components depend upon the arbitrary choice of the coordinate system. It is to be noted particularly, that all variables, flux density, flux, velocities, location and configuration of the circuit, are definitely with respect to the coordinate axes, and may, therefore, be quite different depending on the selection of these axes. It is to be expressly noted, then, that the velocities are *with respect to the reference system* and are not relative velocities between conductor elements and lines of flux. A failure to recognize this implication has been responsible for numerous misinterpretations and much confusion concerning electromagnetic induction.

If the circuit consists of N turns, the induced voltage is N times as great. If several such circuits are connected in series the total induced voltage is the sum of the voltages induced in each circuit, or

$$e = -\sum N\frac{d\phi}{dt} = -\sum N\left(\frac{\partial\phi}{\partial t} + \oint \boldsymbol{B} \cdot \boldsymbol{V} \times d\boldsymbol{s}\right)$$

$$= -\sum N\left(\frac{\partial\phi}{\partial t} + \oint B_n V \sin\theta\, ds\right)$$

$$= -\sum N\left(\frac{\partial\phi}{\partial t} + \oint \begin{vmatrix} \alpha & \beta & \gamma \\ u & v & w \\ dx & dy & dz \end{vmatrix}\right)$$

$$= -\sum N\left(\frac{\partial\phi}{\partial t} + \oint [(\alpha v - \beta u)dz\right.$$

$$\left. + (\beta w - \gamma v)dx + (\gamma u - \alpha w)dy]\right) \quad (40)$$

The case of chief practical interest in electrical machinery is that of a coil with parallel coil sides moving through a field which is uniform in a direction along the coil sides perpendicular to the motion, and is zero along the end connections. Taking the motion along the x-axis, and an effective length of coil l along the z-axis, we have

$$\left.\begin{array}{l} \boldsymbol{B} = \boldsymbol{i}(0) + \boldsymbol{j}\beta + \boldsymbol{k}(0) \\ \boldsymbol{V} = \boldsymbol{i}u + \boldsymbol{j}(0) + \boldsymbol{k}(0) \\ d\boldsymbol{s} = \boldsymbol{i}(0) + \boldsymbol{j}(0) + \boldsymbol{k}\, dz \end{array}\right\} \quad (41)$$

Then substituting Eq. (41) in (40) we find

$$e = -N\left[\frac{\partial\phi}{\partial t} + \oint (j\beta) \cdot (iu) \times (k\,dz)\right]$$

$$= -N\left[\frac{\partial\phi}{\partial t} - \oint \beta u\,dz\right]$$

$$= -N\left[\frac{\partial\phi}{\partial t} + \int_0^l \beta_2 u\,dz + \int_l^0 \beta_1 u\,dz\right]$$

$$= -N\left[\frac{\partial\phi}{\partial t} + l(\beta_2 - \beta_1)u\right] \tag{42}$$

and this is identical with the results arrived at in Eqs. (15) and (17) by other methods.

INDUCED VOLTAGE IN AN ELEMENT OF CIRCUIT

Faraday's law was formulated for *closed circuits*. However, the *motional emf* term of Eq. (40) certainly assigns a definite portion of the total induced voltage to each element of the circuit. The question arises as to whether the *variational component* may not also be expressed in some form which will assign a definite portion of the total voltage to each element of circuit; for if this is possible then the law of induction can be applied to any point in space rather than to a particular closed circuit. There are a number of ways in which this can be done.

From Eq. (24), since C is fixed,

$$e_{\text{variational}} = -\frac{\partial\phi}{\partial t} = -\frac{\partial}{\partial t}\oint A \cdot ds = -\oint\left(\frac{\partial A}{\partial t}\right) \cdot ds \tag{43}$$

Also, since $B \cdot V \times ds = B \times V \cdot ds$, Eq. (39) becomes

$$e = e_{\text{variational}} + e_{\text{motional}} = -\oint\left(\frac{\partial A}{\partial t} + B \times V\right) \cdot ds \tag{44}$$

or by Eq. (21)

$$e = -\oint \left[\frac{\partial A}{\partial t} + (\nabla \times A) \times V \right] \cdot ds \qquad (45)$$

Now if E is the electric gradient around the circuit

$$e = \oint E \cdot ds \qquad (46)$$

To the integrands of Eq. (44) or (45) may be added any acyclic function ∇U, since the line integral of ∇U around any closed path is zero. Such a function exists when no changes are taking place in the magnetic field or circuit, and it is therefore identified physically as the electrostatic potential. Ignoring it and equating the integrands of Eqs. (44), (45), and (46) we get

$$-E = \frac{\partial A}{\partial t} + B \times V = \frac{\partial A}{\partial t} + (\nabla \times A) \times V \qquad (47)$$

This is the gradient, or volts per unit length, induced in each element of the circuit, and depends only on the location and velocity of the circuit element and the behavior of the flux density, or its derived vector potential, at that point. If the circuit is stationary

$$-E = \frac{\partial A}{\partial t} \quad \text{for } C \text{ fixed} \qquad (48)$$

Or upon taking the *curl* of Eq. (48) there results Heaviside's second circuited relationship

$$\nabla \times E = -\frac{\partial}{\partial t}(\nabla \times A) = -\frac{\partial B}{\partial t} \quad \text{for } C \text{ fixed} \qquad (49)$$

The advantage of Eq. (47) or (48) or (49) is that the voltage induced in a *part of a circuit* may be calculated quite independently of other parts of the circuit, if the vector potential is known. The three simultaneous equations

$$\nabla \times A = B \qquad (50)$$

are not sufficient to determine A uniquely. For if A is one solution, $(A + \nabla \psi)$, where $\nabla \psi$ is any acyclic function, is also a solution; since

$$\nabla \times (A + \nabla \psi) = \nabla \times A \qquad (51)$$

The additional condition which Maxwell imposed arbitrarily was

$$\nabla \cdot \boldsymbol{A} = 0 \tag{52}$$

Lorentz and others have imposed different restrictions on the generality of the vector potential, but it would take us too far afield to consider them here.

Several other expressions are possible. For example, applying Stokes' theorem to the line integral of Eq. (44), $\nabla \times \boldsymbol{A} = \boldsymbol{B}$ we find

$$e = -\int\int\left[\frac{\partial \boldsymbol{B}}{\partial t} + \nabla \times (\boldsymbol{B} \times \boldsymbol{V})\right] \cdot \boldsymbol{n}\, dS \tag{53}$$

But

$$\nabla \times (\boldsymbol{B} \times \boldsymbol{V}) = \boldsymbol{B}\,\nabla \cdot \boldsymbol{V} - \boldsymbol{V}\,\nabla \cdot \boldsymbol{B} = \boldsymbol{B}\,\nabla \cdot \boldsymbol{V} \tag{54}$$

since $\nabla \cdot \boldsymbol{B} = 0$, and therefore

$$e = -\int\int\left[\frac{\partial \boldsymbol{B}}{\partial t} + (\nabla \cdot \boldsymbol{V})\boldsymbol{B}\right] \cdot \boldsymbol{n}\, dS \tag{55}$$

THE INDUCED VOLTAGE IN MACHINES

In electrical machines the flux density is perpendicular to the armature surface and may be taken as uniform in the axial direction. Then if l is the axial length of stacking, the flux linked with a coil whose leading and trailing coil sides are at x_2 and x_1 respectively is

$$\phi = \int\int \boldsymbol{n} \cdot \boldsymbol{B}\, dS = \int_0^l\int_{x_1}^{x_2} B(x,t)dx\, dz = l \int_{x_1}^{x_2} B(x,t)\, dx \tag{56}$$

Also, in electrical machines the flux density may be regarded as distributed according to the Fourier series

$$B(x,t) = \sum_{k=1}^{\infty} B_k(t) \sin k\left(\frac{\pi x}{\tau} \pm \gamma_k\right) \tag{57}$$

in which x = distance measured in the peripheral direction
τ = pole pitch
k = order of the space harmonic
B_k = amplitude of the kth harmonic

γ_k = phase angle of the kth harmonic.

Substituting Eq. (57) in (56) and integrating, there results

$$\phi = -\sum_1^\infty \frac{l\tau}{k\pi} B_k(t) \left[\cos k\left(\frac{\pi x_2}{\tau} \pm \gamma_k\right) - \cos k\left(\frac{\pi x_1}{\tau} \pm \gamma_k\right) \right]$$

$$= \sum_1^\infty \frac{2l\tau}{k\pi} B_k(t) \sin \frac{k\pi(x_2 - x_1)}{2\tau} \sin k\left(\frac{x_2 + x_1}{2\tau} \pi \pm \gamma_k\right) \quad (58)$$

But the average value of a sinusoidal (space) distribution is $2/\pi$ times its crest value, and the half-wavelength of the kth harmonic is τ/k. Therefore, the flux in a half-wavelength is

$$\frac{2}{\pi} \frac{\tau}{k} lB_k(t) = \phi_k(t) \quad (59)$$

Now $(x_2 - x_1)$ is the span of the coil, and $(x_2 + x_1)/2 = x_0$ is the location of its midpoint. Then (58) may be rewritten as

$$\phi = \sum_1^\infty \phi_k(t) K_{pk} \sin k\left(\frac{\pi x_0}{\tau} \pm \gamma_k\right) \quad (60)$$

in which

$$K_{pk} = \sin \frac{k\pi}{2\tau}(x_2 - x_1) \quad (61)$$

is the *pitch coefficient* of the coil for the kth harmonic.

In Eq. (60), not only $\phi_k(t)$, but also x_0 and γ_k are, in general, functions of time; for both the coil and the flux may be moving. The induced voltage therefore is

$$e = -N\frac{d\phi}{dt} = -N\left(\frac{\partial\phi}{\partial t} + \frac{\partial\phi}{\partial x_0}\frac{dx_0}{dt} + \frac{\partial\phi}{\partial \gamma_k}\frac{d\gamma_k}{dt}\right)$$

$$= -\sum_1^k NK_{pk} \left\{ \frac{\partial\phi_k}{\partial t} \sin k\left(\frac{\pi x_0}{\tau} \pm \gamma_k\right) \right.$$

$$\left. + k\phi_k\left(\frac{\pi}{\tau}\frac{dx_0}{dt} \pm \frac{d\gamma_k}{dt}\right) \cos k\left(\frac{\pi x_0}{\tau} \pm \gamma_k\right) \right\} \quad (62)$$

APPARATUS	REFERENCE AXES	CIRCUIT CONSIDERED	CHANGE OF FLUX LINKAGES		VOLTAGE GENERATED
			INCREASE	DECREASE	
Transformer	Core	Either	$N\dfrac{\partial\phi}{\partial t}$	$-N\dfrac{\partial\phi}{\partial t}$	a-c
D-c generator	Field	At brushes	$N\phi\dfrac{\pi}{\tau}\dfrac{dx_0}{dt}$	$-\phi\dfrac{dN}{dt}$	d-c
	Armature	At brushes	$N\phi\dfrac{d\gamma}{dt}$	$-\phi\dfrac{dN}{dt}$	d-c
Synchronous generator	Field	Armature	$N\phi\dfrac{\pi}{\tau}\dfrac{dx_0}{dt}$	$-N\phi\dfrac{\pi}{\tau}\dfrac{dx_0}{dt}$	a-c
	Armature	Armature	$N\phi\dfrac{d\gamma}{dt}$	$-N\phi\dfrac{d\gamma}{dt}$	a-c
Polyphase induction motor	Stator	Rotor	$N\phi\left(\dfrac{\pi}{\tau}\dfrac{dx_0}{dt}-\dfrac{d\gamma}{dt}\right)$	$-N\phi\left(\dfrac{\pi}{\tau}\dfrac{dx_0}{dt}-\dfrac{d\gamma}{dt}\right)$	a-c
	Rotor	Rotor	$N\phi\dfrac{d\gamma}{dt}$	$-N\phi\dfrac{d\gamma}{dt}$	a-c
	Rotating synchronously	Rotor	$N\phi\dfrac{\pi}{\tau}\dfrac{dx_0}{dt}$	$-N\phi\dfrac{\pi}{\tau}\dfrac{dx_0}{dt}$	a-c

Here the processes of induction are easily identified with the three terms

$$\left.\begin{array}{ll} \dfrac{\partial \phi_k}{\partial t}, & \text{variation of the space flux} \\[2ex] \dfrac{\pi}{\tau}\dfrac{dx_0}{dt} = \omega_0 t, & \text{movement of the coil} \\[2ex] \dfrac{d\gamma_k}{dt} = \omega_k t, & \text{movement of the field} \end{array}\right\} \qquad (63)$$

In the transformer, the coils are stationary and the flux fixed in position, so the only term is the *variational component*, or transformer action,

$$\partial \phi_k / \partial t$$

In the d-c generator, the field is constant in magnitude and stationary, so that the only term is the *motional component*, or cutting action dx_0/dt.

In the polyphase induction motor, the field is of constant magnitude, but rotating at synchronous speed, so that the voltage induced in the stator winding is due entirely to the term $d\gamma_k/dt = \omega t$.

Equation (62) has, in fact, been made the basis of a comprehensive treatment of machines in another reference.* This matter of voltage induction in the coil of an electrical machine will not be pursued farther here, except that reference may be made to the table on page 37 which shows how the arbitrary choice of reference axes may have considerable effect on the interpretation according to Eq. (62).

* *Alternating Current Machinery* by L. V. Bewley, The Macmillan Company, 1949.

CHAPTER V

GENERAL CRITERIA for ELECTROMAGNETIC INDUCTION

In the light of the definitions and derivations given in the previous chapters it is now possible to formulate general criteria which will enable one to analyze any and all cases of changes in flux linkages and to determine whether or not a voltage will be induced thereby. After these criteria are established it is a relatively simple matter to examine the nature of the various changes in flux linkages that occur in any given case and to ascertain the types of voltage induction which occur.

It has been shown that the flux linkages of a circuit may be changed in two very different ways, either the flux may be varied causing a voltage to be induced according to Faraday's law, or a substitution of circuit may be effected without inducing a voltage. Furthermore, it has been shown that the flux linking an unbroken circuit may be changed either by variation of the magnetic field (transformer action) or by the motion of the circuit through that field (cutting action) and the relative values of these two components depend essentially on the arbitrary choice of reference axes. It also has been shown that both the variational and the motional components of induced voltage may be put in such form as to ascribe a definite portion of the total voltage around the complete circuit to each element of that circuit. Finally, it has been pointed out that the induction of d-c or constant voltage must involve the alternate building-up of flux linkages by increasing the flux through an intact circuit and the reduction of these flux linkages by a substitution of circuit. All these phenomena and interpretations are consolidated on the chart of Fig. 16 and arranged in the form of a "family tree" of changing flux linkages and electromagnetic induction; so that the whole picture can be seen at a glance. Of course, this chart does not by any means exhaust all the possibilities which can be disclosed by various mathematical manipulations, but it does depict those essential to our purposes.

From Fig. 16, and an understanding of the premises on which it is based, the following rules may be formulated as a set of

GENERAL CRITERIA

(A) Choose an arbitrary system of coordinate axes and refer the flux densities, fluxes, position and configuration of the circuit, and velocities to these axes.

(B) If that flux in space linked with the electric circuit at any instant, that is with the circuit intact and fixed, is a function of time with respect to the coordinate axes, it will induce in the circuit a *variational component* of voltage

$$e_v = -\sum N\frac{\partial \phi}{\partial t}$$

where the summation is to include all those groups of concentrated turns of which the complete circuit is composed, and ϕ is the flux linked with each group of N concentrated turns. By "concentrated turns" is understood all those turns connected in series which link exactly the same flux, although they may be physically widely distributed in space. This is also called "transformer action." The voltage gradient E at any point in space due to this variation is given by either of the relationships

$$E_v = -\frac{\partial A}{\partial t}$$

$$\nabla \times E_v = -\frac{\partial B}{\partial t}$$

(C) If any of the elements ds of an electric (conducting) circuit are moving with respect to the coordinate axes so as to "cut" the magnetic flux, there will be induced a *motional component* of voltage

$$e_m = -\Sigma N \oint B_n V \sin \theta \, ds$$

in which V = velocity of the element ds

$\quad\quad \theta$ = angle between V and ds

$\quad\quad B_n$ = component of flux density normal to the plane of V and ds

$\quad\quad \oint$ = the integral completely around the circuit

The voltage gradient E at any point in space due to this motion is given by

$$\boldsymbol{E}_m = -\boldsymbol{B} \times \boldsymbol{V} = -(\nabla \times \boldsymbol{A}) \times \boldsymbol{V}$$

(D) Any change of interlinkages which cannot be classified under either (B) or (C) must be due to a *substitution of circuit dN/dt* and will necessarily involve some switching operation, transfer of turns, or sliding contact; and will always require a discontinuity (break) in the circuit itself. No voltage will be induced thereby; except in so far as the space flux itself may be changed, either because the existing mmf is furnished by the turns or because they happen to be made of a magnetic material whose shifting causes a change in the reluctance of the magnetic paths.

(E) It is impossible to induce a d-c or unidirectional voltage in an uninterrupted circuit. However, a d-c voltage may be obtained by repeatedly building up the flux linkages by methods (B) or (C) and reducing them by method (D). In this way voltages are induced during the increase of flux linkages, but no voltages are induced during their reduction, while the flux linkages are held within finite bounds.

In applying these criteria to a specific case, the procedure is as follows:

(a)   Select the coordinate axes as convenient.

(b)   Consider all motion of the circuit, or substitution of circuit,

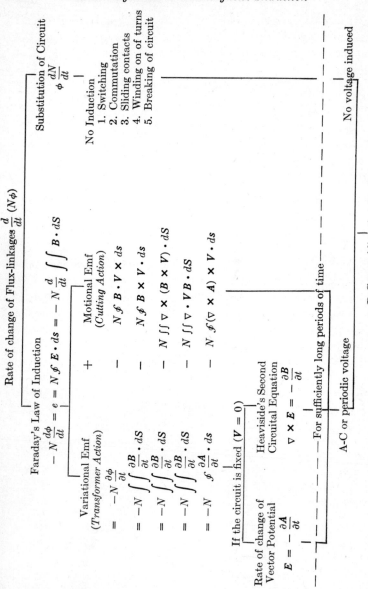

Figure 16.

to cease momentarily and compute the variational component of voltage for each instantaneous position of the circuit. (If the motion of the material of the circuit, for example, an iron cylinder, is responsible for a change of flux in space, then this change of flux in space must be assumed to continue, even though the circuit itself is assumed to be momentarily stopped for the purpose of computing the variational component of voltage.)

(c)   Consider the rate of change of the flux *in space* to be instantaneously stopped and compute the motional component of induced voltage.

(d)   Any change of flux linkages which cannot be charged to either (b) or (c) is credited to a substitution of circuit and is to be identified with the action of some discontinuity in the metallic circuit.

(e)   In every case of d-c voltage induction, identify the substitution of circuit which must occur.

These criteria will be applied to a number of so-called paradoxes in the next chapter, after which it will become evident that they are not at all baffling if one recognizes the true nature of changing flux linkages which occur and their relationship to electromagnetic induction.

CHAPTER VI

APPLICATIONS
and PARADOXES

In this chapter a number of cases will be examined in the light of the definitions, derivations, and criteria developed in the previous chapters. We shall proceed from the simpler to the more complicated cases.

1. FIXED LOOP IN A VARIABLE MAGNETIC FIELD

Figure 17 shows a fixed rigid loop, stationary in space, and interlinked with a variable magnetic flux ϕ. It is obvious that the rate of change of flux linkages, $d\Omega/dt = d\phi/dt$, is due entirely to the

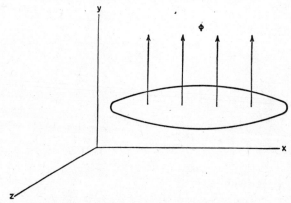

Figure 17. Fixed Loop in Variable Magnetic Field.

varying flux. However, let us apply the criteria in routine fashion:

(A) Take a coordinate system (x,y,z) fixed to the circuit.
(B) The variational component is $e_v = -\partial\phi/\partial t$.
(C) There is no motion, so $e_m = 0$.
(D) The circuit is unbroken, so $dN/dt = 0$ and there is no substitution of circuit.
(E) The voltage cannot be unidirectional.

This is the elementary case of "transformer action."

If $\qquad \phi = \Phi \cos \omega t \qquad$ then $\qquad e = -\dfrac{\partial\phi}{\partial t} = \omega\Phi \sin \omega t$

2. COIL MOVING THROUGH A RIGID DISTRIBUTION OF FLUX

Figure 18 shows a rectangular coil moving through a rigid (unvarying) field of flux. The criteria are:

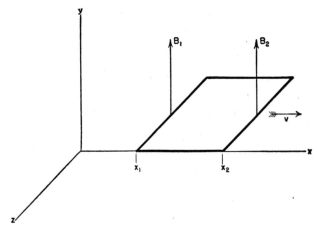

Figure 18. Coil Moving through a Rigid Field.

(A) Take a coordinate system with respect to which the velocity of the coil is V and the flux density is $B(x)$.
(B) The flux is unvarying, so $e_v = 0$.
(C) The leading coil side of length l is located at $x_2(t)$ and is moving at velocity V through flux density $B(x_2)$ while the trailing coil

side of length l is located at $x_1(t)$ and is moving at velocity V through flux density $B(x_1)$. The angle between V and l is $\theta = 90°$, and the component of flux density perpendicular to the plane of the coil is $B_n = B(x)$. Therefore, the motional component is

$$e_m = - \oint B_n V \sin \theta \, ds = \int_0^l B(x_2) V \, ds + \int_l^0 B(x_1) V \, ds$$
$$= (B_2 - B_1) l V$$
$$= (B_2 - B_1) \quad \text{(Area swept out per second by coil side)}$$

(D) The circuit remains intact, and so there is no substitution of circuit.

(E) The voltage cannot be unidirectional, since $(B_2 - B_1)$ cannot increase indefinitely, and there is no substitution of circuit.

3. SLIDING CONTACT

Consider the sliding contact of Fig. 6(c), reproduced here as Fig. 19. The circuit acb is moving to the left at velocity V. Taking

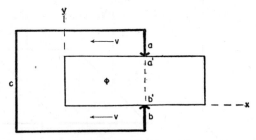

Figure 19. Sliding Contact.

the "instantaneous" circuit to include the path $a'b'$ through the magnet, the general criteria may be applied as follows:

(A) Take the coordinates on the magnetic core (x,y,z).

(B) The flux is constant with respect to (x,y,z), so the variational component of the voltage is $e_v = -\partial\phi/\partial t = 0$.

(C) The metallic external part of the circuit acb is moving at velocity V, but the flux density at all points along the external circuit is zero, so $B = 0$. The geometric line $a'b'$ connecting a to

b through the magnetic core is shifting to the left, but this does not represent a movement of *conducting* material. Hence, where there is movement there is no flux density, and where there is flux density there is no movement, and therefore the motional component of voltage is zero, $e_m = 0$.

(D) The flux linkages are changing. There is no induced voltage. The change in flux linkages must then be due to a substitution of circuit, and the substitution is seen to be taking place at a uniform rate as the sliding contacts a and b move along the core so that the line $a'b'$ through the core is successively changing.

(E) Since there is no voltage induced there is no direct current.

4. HOMOPOLAR INDUCTION

Figure 20 shows the schematic form of the homopolar or unipolar d-c generator. It consists of a bar magnet NS around which revolves a conductor cd on rings R. The circuit is completed through the upper and lower parts of the slip rings and the brushes b, thus forming two circuits in parallel having a common return through the brushes and external circuit. As the conductor revolves, the flux in the upper circuit increases and in the lower circuit correspondingly decreases, but as the flux is in opposite directions relative to the two circuits, the voltage generated is in the same direction. Although the flux through the upper circuit is apparently continually increasing, yet when the conductor reaches the brushes, the flux included is the same as it was a revolution previously.

The paradox may be explained by reference to Fig. 20(c). Let the conductor cd be moved from A to B across the magnet face, generating a voltage. If this conductor could by some means be transferred back to A, each time that it reaches B, and in such a manner that the flux is not cut in a reversed direction or the circuit interrupted, then conditions would be ideal for generating a d-c voltage. The unipolar machine is just such an automatic arrangement for instantaneously effecting a change of interlinkages by a substitution of circuit, and in this respect Fig. 20(c) may be considered as its "development."

In effect, the unipolar machine is equivalent to making the distance AB infinite. But this equivalence is not offered as an explanation of the phenomena of induction in the unipolar generator, for

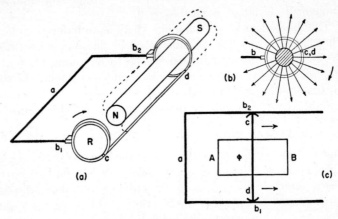

Figure 20. Homopolar Induction.

it fails to take into account the actual substitution of circuit which occurs, *an essential feature of any dynamo-electric machine generating direct current.*

Applying the interlinkage criteria:

(A) Choose axes on the frame.
(B) There is no change of flux, hence no voltage $\partial \phi / \partial t$.
(C) The moving element cuts flux and always in the same direction, thus inducing a unidirectional voltage Blv.
(D) There is an automatic substitution of circuit each time that the conductor passes under the brush.
(E) The interlinkages are increased at a regular rate by cutting the flux and induce a unidirectional voltage; but the interlinkages are reduced to zero by a substitution of circuit each time that the conductor passes under the brush. Thus a d-c voltage is continuously generated.

A UNIQUE D-C GENERATOR

The most familiar d-c generator is the ordinary commutator machine having a constant field flux fixed in space. In such machines the induced voltage is purely motional, and the commutator functions as an automatic switching device for the continuous substitution of circuit. In the homopolar d-c generator described in the previous article the induced voltage is also purely motional, and the substitution of circuit is effected automatically every time the rotating conductor passes under the brushes bearing on the slip rings.

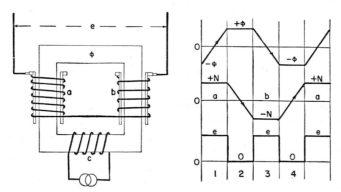

Figure 21. A D-C Generator.

The question naturally arises as to whether it might be possible to induce a unidirectional voltage by transformer action and effect the necessary substitution of circuit by whatever means might be required. Obviously, the flux would have to increase at a uniform rate, that is,

$$e_v = -\frac{\partial \phi}{\partial t} = -\frac{\phi_2 - \phi_1}{t_2 - t_1}$$

And the substitution of circuit would have to reduce the flux linkages from the final value ϕ_2 to the initial value ϕ_1.

An arrangement which achieves these results, shown in Fig. 21, consists of a magnetic core with an exciting winding c and reversible revolving winding drums a and b. Let the flux cycle in the core, furnished by the exciting winding c, be a trapezoidal wave as shown in the sketch, and let it be possible to revolve the drums in such a direction that the turns can be transferred back and forth between drums a and b. Then the generating cycle can be divided into four periods, as follows:

PERIOD	TURNS	FLUX	VOLTAGE
1	N on a, 0 on b	$-\phi$ linearly to $+\phi$	e = constant
2	Transferred from a to b	constant at $+\phi$	$e = 0$
3	0 on a, $-N$ on b	$+\phi$ linearly to $-\phi$	e = constant
4	Transferred from b to a	constant at $-\phi$	$e = 0$

Of course, whether the voltage induced during period 3 is of the same or different sign to that generated during period 1 depends on the direction of the windings, and this is arbitrary. Also, in such a machine, it would be necessary to split the slip rings to prevent short-circuit currents from being induced in them. By operating two such machines in series so that one would be generating when the other was not, the two sets of pulsating unidirectional voltages could be made to add up to a constant d-c voltage.

In the light of the General Criteria, applied to this machine, we have:

(A) Reference axes taken on the core.

(B) There is a variational or transformer component of induced voltage $e = -N \, \partial\phi/\partial t = constant$, during the variation of flux.

(C) No moving conductor cuts the flux, so the motional component of voltage is zero.

(D) The flux linkages are $(+N)(-\phi) = -N\phi$ at the beginning and $(+N)(+\phi) = +N\phi$ at the end of period 1. But the transfer of turns during period 2, when the flux is constant, reduces the flux linkage back to $(-N)(+\phi) = -N\phi$.

(E) Thus the change of flux linkages by $N\,\partial\phi/\partial t$, (B), in combination with the substitution of circuit, (D), permits the induction of a unidirectional voltage.

THE OSCILLATING BAR GENERATOR

In Fig. 22 is shown an arrangement in which a harmonic motion

$$u = \omega r \cos \omega t$$

is imparted to a bar ab by cranks c and d of radius r, time being counted from the instant when the bar is in its mid-position. The bar moves back and forth through a uniform field of width $2r$ and density

$$\beta = B \cos \omega t$$

What is the voltage induced in the circuit $abcd$?

(A) Select reference axes (x,y,z) on the magnetic core.
(B) At any instant t the flux included by the circuit is $\phi = lr(1 - \sin \theta) B \cos \omega t$ in which $\theta = \omega t$ is the crank angle. Stopping the motion at this instant ($\theta = $ constant), the variational component of voltage is

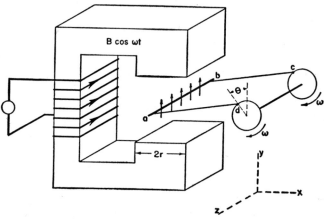

Figure 22. Oscillating Bar Generator.

$$e_v = -\frac{\partial \phi}{\partial t} = \omega Blr(1 - \sin \theta) \sin \omega t$$

$$= \omega Blr(1 - \sin \omega t) \sin \omega t$$

$$= \omega Blr(\sin \omega t - \sin^2 \omega t)$$

(C) The motional component of voltage is

$$e_m = +\beta lu = (B \cos \omega t) \, l\omega r \cos \omega t$$

$$= \omega Blr \cos^2 \omega t$$

(D) No substitution of circuit can occur, since the circuit is never interrupted.

The total voltage is the sum of the variational and motional components, or

$$e = e_v + e_m = \omega Blr(\sin \omega t - \sin^2 \omega t + \cos^2 \omega t)$$

$$= \omega Blr(\sin \omega t + \cos 2\omega t)$$

$$= \omega \frac{\Phi}{2}(\sin \omega t + \cos 2\omega t)$$

The apparatus is a double-frequency a-c generator.

Since no substitution of circuit is involved to mask the result, there is no difficulty in calculating the voltage directly from the rate of change of flux, thus

$$e = -\frac{d\phi}{dt} = -\frac{d}{dt}[Blr(1 - \sin \omega t) \cos \omega t]$$

$$= \omega Blr(\sin \omega t - \sin^2 \omega t + \cos^2 \omega t)$$

$$= \omega Blr(\sin \omega t + \cos 2\omega t)$$

THE SWINGING BAR GENERATOR*

Figure 23 illustrates a pendulum arrangement in which a bar ab of length l on a radius R swings back and forth with horizontal velocity $u = \omega R \cos \omega t$ in an alternating field of density

* "Electrical Essays for Recreation" by H. Sohon, *Electrical Engineering*, vol. 64, 1945, p. 294.

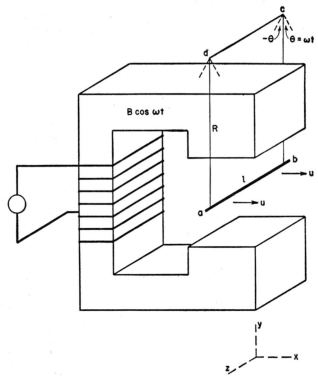

Figure 23. Swinging Bar Generator.

$$\beta = B \cos \omega t$$

counting time from the instant when the bar is in its mean position. The amplitude of swing is supposed to be small so that the flux linked with the circuit *abcd* is

$$\phi = (lR \sin \theta)(B \cos \omega t)$$

(A) Select reference axes (x, y, z) on the core.

(B) Consider the motion to be stopped at any angle $\theta = \omega t$. Then the variational component of voltage is

$$e_v = -\frac{\partial \phi}{\partial t} = \omega BlR \sin \omega t \sin \theta$$

$$= \omega BlR \sin^2 \omega t$$

$$= \tfrac{1}{2}\omega BlR(1 - \cos 2\omega t)$$

(C) The motional component of voltage is

$$e_m = -\beta lu = -(B \cos \omega t)l(\omega R \cos \omega t)$$

$$= -\omega BlR \cos^2 \omega t$$

$$= -\tfrac{1}{2}\omega BlR(\cos 2\omega t + 1)$$

(D) No substitution of circuit can occur, since the circuit is never broken.

The total voltage is the sum of the variational and motional components, or

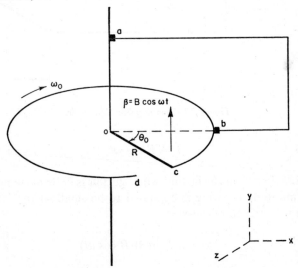

Figure 24. Single-Spoke Wheel.

$$e = e_v + e_m = -\omega BlR \cos 2\omega t$$

Since no substitution of circuit occurs to mask the result, the voltage may also be calculated directly from the total rate of change of flux, thus

$$e = -\frac{d\phi}{dt} = -\frac{d}{dt}(lRB \sin \omega t \cos \omega t)$$

$$= -\omega BlR \cos 2\omega t$$

The apparatus generates a second harmonic voltage.

It is interesting to note that both the variational and motional parts of the voltage contain equal components of d-c, as well as second harmonics, but the d-c components cancel while the second harmonics add.

SINGLE-SPOKE WHEEL

Figure 24 shows a single-spoke wheel, the rim of which is cut, revolving at angular velocity ω_0 in a uniform pulsating magnetic field of density

$$\beta = B \cos \omega t$$

A brush a bears on the shaft and a second brush b bears on the rim. It is required to determine the voltage generated in the circuit *oabco*.

(A) Select stationary axes (x,y,z).

(B) Assume the motion to be stopped at the instant when the spoke *oc* of radius R has turned off an angle $\theta_0 = \omega_0 t$ from the reference line *ob*. Then the flux linked with the circuit at this instant is that included by the pie-shaped sector *obc*, and is

$$\phi = \tfrac{1}{2}R^2\theta_0 B \cos \omega t$$

The variational component of voltage then is

$$e_v = -\frac{\partial\phi}{\partial t} = \tfrac{1}{2}R^2\theta_0\omega B \sin \omega t$$

for $0 \leq (\theta_0 = \omega_0 t) \leq 2\pi$.

(C) The motional component of the voltage generated in an element of the spoke dr moving at a velocity $r\omega_0$ is $-\beta\omega_0 r\,dr$. The voltage due to cutting action for the whole spoke then is

$$e_m = -\int_0^R \beta\omega_0 r\,dr = -\beta\omega_0\frac{R^2}{2} = -\frac{BR^2}{2}\,\omega_0\cos\omega t$$

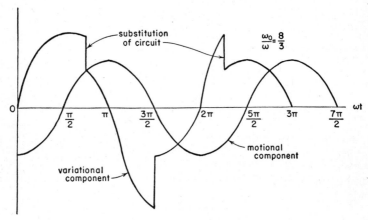

Figure 25. Voltage of the Single-Spoke Wheel When $\omega_0/\omega = 8/3$.

(D) But it is clear that the flux linkages will continue to increase, due both to transformer and cutting action, only until the spoke oc has made one complete revolution and has reached position ob. As soon as the spoke passes brush b the flux linkages are reduced to zero, and a new cycle begins. Thus there is a substitution of circuit at this instant, a new circuit $oabco$ is substituted for the old circuit $oabdco$ as the brush breaks contact with point d and makes contact with point c.

(E) The total voltage is the sum of the variational and motional components,

$$e = e_v + e_m = \frac{BR^2}{2}(\omega\theta_0\sin\omega t - \omega_0\cos\omega t)$$

for $0 \leq (\theta_0 = \omega_0 t) \leq 2\pi$. Each time that the spoke passes the brush b, the angle θ_0 starts anew from zero. The voltage is thus a discontinuous function, as illustrated in Fig. 25.

The total voltage, up until the instant when a substitution of circuit occurs, may be calculated directly from the rate of change of the flux

$$e = -\frac{d\phi}{dt}$$

$$= \frac{BR^2}{2}\left(\omega\theta_0 \sin \omega t - \frac{d\theta_0}{dt} \cos \omega t\right)$$

$$= \frac{BR^2}{2}(\omega\theta_0 \sin \omega t - \omega_0 \cos \omega t)$$

for $0 \leq (\theta_0 = \omega_0 t) \leq 2\pi$

The reason for the interrupted rim in this problem was to avoid having a second circuit (the completed rim) in the problem. Such a complete rim would constitute a short-circuited turn to the pulsating flux and would have a transformer (but no cutting action) voltage induced in it.

MULTIPLE-SPOKE WHEEL

Consider the case of a multiple-spoke wheel with the rim cut between every pair of spokes, revolving at angular velocity ω_0 in a uniform pulsating magnetic field of density

$$\beta = B \cos \omega t$$

A brush a bears on the shaft, and a second brush b bears on the rim at a fixed angle $\theta_0 = \theta_1$ from the reference line ob'. It is required to determine the voltage generated in the circuit $oabco$.

(A) Select stationary axes (x,y,z).
(B) Assume the motion to be stopped. The flux linked with the circuit is that in the pie-shaped sector $ob'b$,

$$\phi = \tfrac{1}{2}R^2\theta_0 B \cos \omega t$$

The variational component of flux then is, since $\theta_0 = \theta_1$,

$$e_v = -\frac{\partial \phi}{\partial t} = \frac{BR^2}{2}\theta_1\omega \sin \omega t$$

or a simple alternating voltage (since $\theta_1 = $ constant).

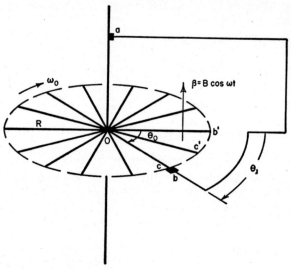

Figure 26. Multiple-Spoke Wheel.

(C) The motional component of voltage is, since the spokes have an angular velocity ω_0,

$$e_m = -\int_0^R \beta\omega_0 r\,dr = -\beta\omega_0\frac{R^2}{2} = -\frac{BR^2}{2}\omega_0 \cos \omega t$$

(D) A substitution of circuit is observed to take place each time a particular spoke oc moves out from under the brush b and is replaced by the next spoke oc'. Thus the *increase* of flux linkages brought about by the movement of the spoke through the field is nullified by the *decrease* in flux linkages due to the successive substitution of new spokes for old.

(E) The total voltage is

$$e = e_v + e_m = \frac{BR^2}{2}(\theta_1\omega \sin \omega t - \omega_0 \cos \omega t)$$

This alternating voltage has the same motional component as for the single-spoke case, but its variational component is different.

If the flux is constant ($\omega = 0$), the voltage becomes

$$e = -\frac{BR^2}{2}\omega_0$$

and the apparatus is seen to generate direct current.

The total voltage can also be calculated directly from the rate of change of flux linkages

$$e = -\frac{d\phi}{dt} = \frac{BR^2}{2}\left(\theta_0\omega \sin \omega t - \frac{d\theta_0}{dt} \cos \omega t\right)$$

Now $\theta_0 = \theta_1$ is constant, but the instantaneous angular velocity of the moving spoke is

$$\frac{d\theta_0}{dt} = \omega_0$$

Hence the voltage is

$$e = \frac{BR^2}{2}(\theta_1\omega \sin \omega t - \omega_0 \cos \omega t)$$

agreeing with the result found by adding the variational and motional components.

If brush b is at b', so that $\theta_1 = 0$, the variational component of the voltage vanishes and only the motional component survives.

A "UNIVERSAL GENERATOR"

In Fig. 27 there is shown a machine consisting of a revolving magnet M and a revolving segmented wheel W upon which bears a moving brush b. The rim of the wheel is broken between spokes so as to avoid eddy currents within the wheel itself. The spool s, with its slip ring and brush, performs no electrical function and is

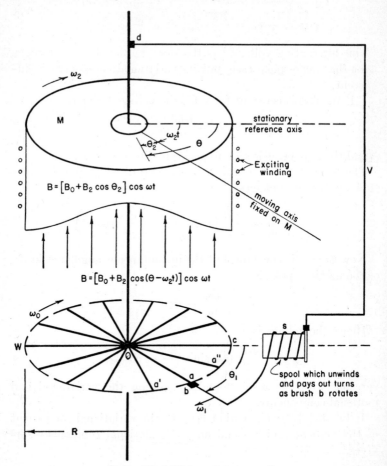

Figure 27. A "Universal Generator."

intended merely as a means of paying out line to the moving brush *b*. The face of the magnet *M* is so shaped and its excitation is such as to provide a flux density

$$B = (B_0 + B_2 \cos \theta_2) \cos \omega t$$

in which B_0 = uniform component of flux density

B_2 = harmonic component of flux density

θ_2 = angle measured from moving axis fixed on the magnet

With respect to the stationary reference axis

$$\theta_2 = \theta - \omega_2 t$$

where θ = angle measured from the stationary axis

ω_2 = angular velocity of the revolving magnet

The flux density may then be expressed as

$$B = [B_0 + B_2 \cos (\theta - \omega_2 t)] \cos \omega t$$

The total flux linked with the circuit *oabsVdo* is the flux through the pie-shaped sector *oac,* and is

$$\phi = \int_0^{\theta_1} B \frac{R^2}{2} d\theta = \frac{R^2}{2} \int_0^{\theta_1} [B_0 + B_2 \cos (\theta - \omega_2 t)] \cos \omega t \, d\theta$$

$$= \frac{R^2}{2} [B_0 \theta_1 + B_2 \sin (\theta_1 - \omega_2 t) + B_2 \sin \omega_2 t] \cos \omega t$$

in which $\theta_1 = \omega_1 t$ for a moving brush

θ_1 = *constant* for a stationary brush

This would appear to be a complicated case, since the flux is pulsating as well as rotating, conductors are moving through and cutting the flux, and substitutions of circuit are occurring not only because of the commutator segments, but also because of the winding on of turns by the revolving brush. However, the General Criteria gives the voltage equation in a few lines in routine fashion.

(A) Select stationary reference axes (x,y,z).

(B) Stop the motion of the conductors ($\omega_0 = 0$) and the substitutions of circuit ($\omega_1 = 0$ or $\theta_1 = $ constant). Then the variational component of voltage is

$$e_v = -\frac{\partial \phi}{\partial t} = \frac{R^2}{2} \{ + \omega_2 [B_2 \cos (\theta_1 - \omega_2 t) - B_2 \cos \omega_2 t] \cos \omega t$$

$$+ \omega [B_0 \theta_1 + B_2 \sin (\theta_1 - \omega_2 t) + B_2 \sin \omega_2 t] \sin \omega t \}$$

MACHINE	B_0	B_2	ω	ω_0	ω_1	ω_2	θ_1	EQUATION OF VOLTAGE
Transformer	B_0	0	ω	0	0	0	$2\pi N$	$+\pi R^2 B_0 N \omega \sin \omega t$
D-c generator	B_0	0	0	ω_0	0	0	0	$-\frac{1}{2} R^2 B_0 \omega_0$
A-c generator	0	B_2	0	0	0	ω_2	θ_1	$-\frac{1}{2} R^2 B_2 \omega_2 [\cos \omega_2 t - \cos(\theta_1 - \omega_2 t)]$
Slip-freq. generator	0	B_2	0	ω_0	ω_0	ω_2	$\omega_0 t$	$-\frac{1}{2} R^2 B_2 [\omega_2 \cos \omega_2 t + (\omega_0 - \omega_2) \cos (\omega_0 - \omega_2)t]$
A-c generator	0	B_2	0	ω_0	ω_2	ω_2	$\omega_2 t + \pi/2$	$-\frac{1}{2} R^2 B_2 \omega_2 \cos \omega_2 t$
Vibrator	B_0	0	0	$\sin \omega' t$	0	0	0	$-\frac{1}{2} R^2 B_0 \sin \omega' t$

(C) The motional component of voltage is, since $\theta = \theta_1$ for spoke oa

$$e_m = -\oint \mathbf{B} \times \mathbf{V} \cdot d\mathbf{s} = -\int_0^R Br\omega_0 \, dr$$

$$= -\frac{R^2}{2}\omega_0[B_0 + B_2 \cos(\theta_1 - \omega_2 t)] \cos \omega t$$

(D) One substitution of circuit is evident as the spokes pass brush b at a relative velocity $(\omega_0 - \omega_1)$, for then the circuit involves spokes oa', oa, and oa'' in succession. Another substitution of circuit is evident as turns accumulate around the flux due to the rotating brush b and the line unwound from spool s.

(E) The total voltage is the sum of the variational and motional components

$$e = e_v + e_m = -\frac{R^2}{2}\{B_0(\omega_0 \cos \omega t - \theta_1 \omega \sin \omega t)$$

$$+ B_2[(\omega_0 - \omega_2) \cos(\theta_1 - \omega_2 t) \cos \omega t + \omega_2 \cos \omega_2 t \cos \omega t$$

$$- \omega \sin(\theta_1 - \omega_2 t) \sin \omega t - \omega \sin \omega_2 t \sin \omega t]\}$$

This apparatus exhibits:

1. Generation by transformer action due to the pulsating flux density $B_0 \cos \omega t$.
2. Generation by the revolving field $B_2 \cos(\theta - \omega_2 t)$.
3. Generation by the moving conductors cutting the flux (ω_0).
4. Substitution of circuits as the spokes pass the brush b. (oa', oa, oa'' in succession).
5. Substitution of circuits as the turns accumulate on account of the rotating brush ($\theta_1 = 2\pi N$).

There are innumerable special cases included by this machine, a few of which are given in the table on page 62.

THE FARADAY DISK

The first rotating machine to generate a voltage electromagnetically was Faraday's disk. But to this day it is probably the least understood of all electric generators. Its theory of operation has been a controversial subject from the beginning, and articles

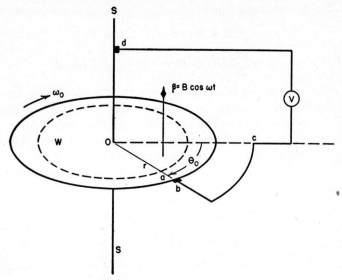

Figure 28. The Faraday Disk.

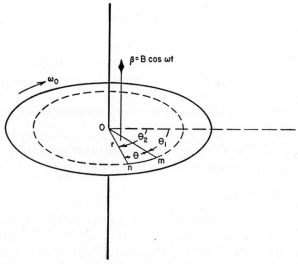

Figure 29. The Faraday Disk.

discussing it appear regularly in the technical press. The arrangement, Fig. 28, consists of a solid disk W revolving at an angular velocity ω_0 on shaft S in a uniform magnetic field β. A brush b bears on the rim of the disk, and a second brush d bears on the shaft. In Faraday's original machine the field was constant, as well as uniform, but more general conditions are introduced by taking the field as alternating,

$$\beta = B \cos \omega t$$

and assuming the brush b at an angle θ_0 from the plane $ocVd$ of the external circuit.

First of all, let us mark out a sector-shaped circuit omn on the disk, Fig. 29, in which the arms om and on are of radius r and are at a fixed angle θ apart. Since the disk is revolving, the arms om and on make angles $\theta_1 = \omega_0 t$ and $\theta_2 = \theta + \omega_0 t$ with the reference line. The flux included by this sector-shaped circuit at any instant is

$$\phi = \tfrac{1}{2}r^2(\theta_2 - \theta_1)B \cos \omega t = \tfrac{1}{2}r^2\theta B \cos \omega t = \frac{\theta}{2\pi}\Phi \cos \omega t$$

Since the circuit is definite, and never interrupted, the voltage induced is

$$e = -\frac{d\phi}{dt} = \tfrac{1}{2}r^2B\left[\omega(\theta_2 - \theta_1)\sin \omega t - \left(\frac{d\theta_2}{dt} - \frac{d\theta_1}{dt}\right)\cos \omega t\right]$$

But $\theta_2 - \theta_1 = \theta$ (a constant), and

$$\frac{d\theta_2}{dt} = \frac{d\theta_1}{dt} = \omega_0$$

so that the induced voltage reduces to

$$e = \tfrac{1}{2}r^2B\omega\theta \sin \omega t = \omega\frac{\theta}{2\pi}\Phi \sin \omega t$$

This is identical with the variational component of induced voltage

$$e_v = -\frac{\partial\phi}{\partial t} = \omega\frac{\theta}{2\pi}\Phi \sin \omega t$$

This variational, or transformer, voltage is seen to increase with the angle θ, and to become a maximum when $\theta = 2\pi$. Evidently this component of voltage is entirely circumferential and will cause circular currents to flow in the disk just sufficient to consume it; for which reason it cannot appear in the external circuit.

The terms involving $d\theta_2/dt = \omega_0$ and $d\theta_1/dt = \omega_0$, which cancelled each other, correspond to the motional components of voltage in arms *on* and *om* respectively. Either arm has a voltage

$$e_m = \int_0^r \beta\omega_0 r \, dr = \frac{\omega_0}{2}r^2\beta = \frac{\omega_0}{2}r^2 B \cos \omega t$$

Each of these motional components, being directed radially toward the shaft, cancels in going around the circuit *omn*. Thus every radius on the disk has the same motional component of voltage directed radially towards the center, and consequently the entire periphery of the disk is at the same voltage due to its motion.

As far as the external circuit is concerned, only the motional component of voltage,

$$e_m = \frac{\omega_0}{2}R^2 B \cos \omega t$$

survives, the variational component being consumed by the eddy currents which it produces.

If the disk is split up into a large number of sectors insulated from each other, the eddy currents cannot flow, and the transformer component of voltage also will then appear in the external circuit. The analysis and results are the same as for the multiple-spoke wheel given in a previous section.

It is of interest to investigate the direction of the *voltage gradient* in the disk. This is given by Eq. (47) as

$$-\boldsymbol{E} = -\boldsymbol{E}_v - \boldsymbol{E}_m = \frac{\partial \boldsymbol{A}}{\partial t} + \boldsymbol{B} \times \boldsymbol{V}$$

in which the vector potential A is defined by

$$\left. \begin{array}{c} \nabla \times \boldsymbol{A} = \boldsymbol{B} \\ \nabla \cdot \boldsymbol{A} = 0 \end{array} \right\}$$

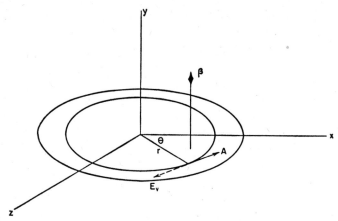

Figure 30. The Faraday Disk.

Referring to Fig. 30 the flux inside the circle of radius r is $\phi = \pi r^2 B \cos \omega t$. The total variational component of voltage around the circle of radius r is

$$e_v = -\frac{\partial \phi}{\partial t} = \pi r^2 \omega B \sin \omega t$$

and the gradient, in the plane of the disk, is

$$E_v = \frac{e_v}{2\pi r} = \frac{r}{2}\omega B \sin \omega t$$

The variational component of the gradient is given by $-\partial A/\partial t$ and therefore E_v and A have opposite directions, and A is proportional to $r = \sqrt{x^2 + z^2}$. We may infer, therefore, from Fig. 30 and the foregoing that

$$A = \sqrt{A_x{}^2 + A_z{}^2} = \frac{r}{2}\beta = \frac{\sqrt{x^2 + z^2}}{2}\beta$$

$$A_x = A \sin \theta = A\frac{z}{\sqrt{x^2 + z^2}} = \frac{\beta}{2}z$$

$$A_y = 0$$

$$A_z = -A \cos \theta = -A\frac{x}{\sqrt{x^2 + z^2}} = -\frac{\beta}{2}x$$

Substituting these values in the expressions for the *curl* and *divergence* of the vector potential, we have

$$\begin{cases} \dfrac{\partial A_z}{\partial y} - \dfrac{\partial A_y}{\partial z} = 0 \\[2mm] \dfrac{\partial A_x}{\partial z} - \dfrac{\partial A_z}{\partial x} = \dfrac{\beta}{2} + \dfrac{\beta}{2} = \beta \\[2mm] \dfrac{\partial A_y}{\partial x} - \dfrac{\partial A_x}{\partial y} = 0 \\[2mm] \dfrac{\partial A_x}{\partial x} + \dfrac{\partial A_y}{\partial y} + \dfrac{\partial A_z}{\partial z} = 0 \end{cases}$$

Thus the differential equations are satisfied, and we have

$$A = iA_x + jA_y + kA_z = i\frac{\beta z}{2} + j0 - k\frac{\beta x}{2}$$

$$= \beta\frac{r}{2}\left(i\frac{z}{r} - k\frac{x}{r}\right) = B\frac{r}{2}(i \sin\theta - k \cos\theta) \cos\omega t$$

The variational component of the gradient then is

$$E_v = -\frac{\partial A}{\partial t} = -\tfrac{1}{2}(iz + j0 - kx)\frac{\partial\beta}{\partial t} = \omega\frac{B}{2}(iz + j0 - kx) \sin\omega t$$

$$= \omega B\frac{r}{2}\left(i\frac{z}{r} + j0 - k\frac{x}{r}\right) \sin\omega t = \omega B\frac{r}{2}(i \sin\theta - k \cos\theta) \sin\omega t$$

Thus the magnitude of E_v is proportional to the radius r, while its direction is seen to be around the circle in the clockwise direction.

The motional component of the electric gradient is

$$E_m = -B \times V = -(i0 + j\beta + k0) \times (-i\omega_0 z + j0 + k\omega_0 x)$$

$$= -\beta\omega_0(ix + kz) = -\beta\omega_0 r\left(i\frac{x}{r} + k\frac{z}{r}\right)$$

$$= -\omega_0 rB\left(i\frac{x}{r} + k\frac{z}{r}\right) \cos\omega t$$

$$= -\omega_0 rB(i \cos\theta + k \sin\theta) \cos\omega t$$

Thus the magnitude of E_m is proportional to the radius r, while its direction is seen to be along the radius toward the center.

WIRE IN ZERO RESULTANT MAGNETIC FIELD

An interesting example of how a misconception may exist about "cutting action" is provided by the situation shown in Fig. 31.* In Fig. 31(a), a N-pole above the conductor is shown moving to the left, and taking the flux density to be "cutting" the conductor

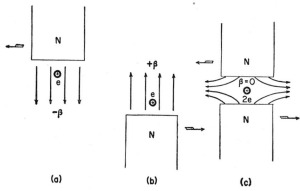

Figure 31. "Superposition."

one arrives at a voltage e directed into the paper. In Fig. 31(b), the N-pole is below the conductor and moving to the right, and the induced voltage is again e and directed into the paper. Now suppose, Fig. 31(c), that two N-poles, one above the conductor and moving to the left, and the other below the conductor and moving to the right, are used as shown on the right. What is the voltage? Here the flux density is zero, and yet by the principle of superposition the voltage should be $2e$! The fallacy in the above reasoning is that the voltages induced in the conductor are *variational* and not *motional* (cutting action) components at all. If ref-

* "Calculation of Induced Voltages in Metallic Conductors" by H. B. Dwight, *Trans. A.I.E.E.*, vol. 49, 1930.

erence axes are taken on the conductor, it is the field that is varying, and not the conductor moving. How then may the voltage induced in the conductor be calculated, since no closed circuit is involved?*

Let the flux density distributions due to the two oppositely moving poles be expressed as traveling waves, so that

$$B = ia + j\beta + k\gamma = i0 + j[f_1(x + v_1t) + f_2(x - v_2t)] + k0$$

Here, both the flux density space distributions and their velocities may be different, as indicated in Fig. 32. Now Heaviside's second circuital relationship for a fixed circuit, given in Eq. (49), is

$$\nabla \times E = -\frac{\partial B}{\partial t}$$

and expanded this becomes

$$
\begin{cases}
\dfrac{\partial E_z}{\partial y} - \dfrac{\partial E_y}{\partial z} = 0 \\[2mm]
\dfrac{\partial E_x}{\partial z} - \dfrac{\partial E_z}{\partial x} = -v_1 f_1(x + v_1t) + v_2 f_2(x - v_2t) \\[2mm]
\dfrac{\partial E_y}{\partial x} - \dfrac{\partial E_x}{\partial y} = 0
\end{cases}
$$

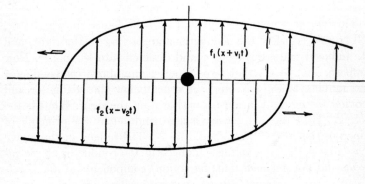

Figure 32. Traveling Waves of Flux Density.

* "Discussion" by L. V. Bewley, *Trans. A.I.E.E.*, vol. 49, 1930.

These partial differential equations have as a solution, compatible with the implied boundary conditions,

$$\left\{ \begin{array}{l} E_x = 0 \\ E_y = 0 \\ E_z = v_1 f_1(x + v_1 t) - v_2 f_2(x - v_2 t) \end{array} \right.$$

But this is the same result as is obtained by applying the "cutting" rule separately to each component of flux density wave and superimposing the results. In particular, if $f_2 = -f_1$, and if $v_2 = v_1$, there is no flux density

$$\beta(o,t) = f_1(0 + v_1 t) + f_2(0 - v_2 t) = 0$$

at the conductor, although the voltage is

$$e = lE_z = l[v_1 f_1(0 + v_1 t) - v_2 f_2(0 - v_2 t)] = 2lv_1 f_1(v_1 t)$$

or twice the voltage for either wave alone. Thus the superposition of voltages calculated on the basis of *relative* motion works in this case, whereas if flux densities are superimposed first there is no possibility of using the "cutting" rule. However, the whole idea of "cutting action" is basically wrong in this case, and the induction is actually a pure example of variational induction.

CONCENTRIC IRON CYLINDER SURROUNDING A WIRE*

Figure 33 shows three cases of an iron cylinder concentric to a current-carrying wire and an associated external circuit *abcd*. In each case the center wire carries a current I, and its magnetomotive force $0.4\pi I$ will cause a flux density (ignoring the thin slot in *c*)

$$B = \frac{0.4\pi I \mu}{2\pi r} = \frac{0.2 I \mu}{r}$$

at radius r in the iron cylinder of permeability μ. This flux density consists of two parts:

* "An Experiment on Electromagnetic Induction by Linear Motion," by E. C. Cullewich, *Journal of Institute of Electrical Engineers* (London), vol. 85, August 1939, pp. 315–18.

$$B_0 = \frac{0.2I}{r} \quad \text{in air}$$

$$B_i = \frac{0.2I}{r}(\mu - 1) \quad \text{additional density due to the iron}$$

Taking $ab = cd = (r_2 - r_1)$, and a length y of the cylinder within the circuit, the total flux linkages with the circuit $abcd$ are

$$(N\phi) = y \int_{r_1}^{r_2} B \, dr + (l - y) \int_{r_1}^{r_2} B_0 \, dr$$

$$= [\mu y + (l - y)] \, 0.2I \log \frac{r_2}{r_1}$$

Case a

Now consider Fig. 33(a) in which the iron cylinder is stationary and the circuit $abcd$ is moving downward at velocity v.

(A) Select stationary axes (x,y,z).

(B) The flux is constant and fixed in space so there is no variational component, $\partial\phi/\partial t = 0$.

(C) The moving conductor ab is cutting flux density B_0 at velocity v, hence the motional component is

$$e_m = v \int_{r_1}^{r_2} B_0 \, dr = v 0.2I \log \frac{r_2}{r_1}$$

(D) The sliding contacts c and d move along the iron cylinder increasing the flux linkages. In doing so the imaginary line cd changes position, but there is no cutting of flux by a material conductor, and the change in flux linkage is due to a substitution of circuit, thus

$$\phi \frac{dN}{dt} = v \int_{r_1}^{r_2} B \, dr = v\mu 0.2I \log \frac{r_2}{r_1}$$

(E) The total voltage induced is that due to the moving conductor ab and is

$$e = e_m = v 0.2I \log \frac{r_2}{r_1}$$

But the total rate of change of flux linkages is

$$\frac{d(N\phi)}{dt} = \frac{d}{dt} [\mu y + (l - y)] \, 0.2I \log \frac{r_2}{r_1}$$

$$= (\mu - 1) \frac{dy}{dt} \, 0.2I \log \frac{r_2}{r_1}$$

$$= (\mu - 1)v0.2I \log \frac{r_2}{r_1}$$

$$= \phi\frac{dN}{dt} - e_m$$

Case b

Consider next the case of Fig. 33(b), which is exactly the same as *Case a*, except that the circuit is now stationary while the iron cylinder moves.

(A) Select stationary axes (x,y,z).

(B) The flux inside the circuit *abcd* is changing by the amount contributed by the iron, hence the variational component of voltage is

$$e_v = -\frac{\partial\phi}{\partial t} = -\frac{\partial}{\partial t}y \int_{r_1}^{r_2} B_i \, dr$$

$$= -\frac{\partial y}{\partial t}(\mu - 1)0.2I \log \frac{r_2}{r_1}$$

$$= -v(\mu - 1)0.2I \log \frac{r_2}{r_1}$$

(C) The line *cd* is now a metallic conductor moving at velocity v in a field of flux density B, and the motional component of voltage therefore is

$$e_m = v \int_{r_1}^{r_2} B \, dr = v\mu0.2I \log \frac{r_2}{r_1}$$

(D) The movement of the cylinder results in the continual substitution of new lines of conducting material *cd* for old lines, and this substitution of circuit results in a rate of change of flux linkages equal to

$$\phi \frac{dN}{dt} = v \int_{r_1}^{r_2} B \, dr = v\mu 0.2I \log \frac{r_2}{r_1}$$

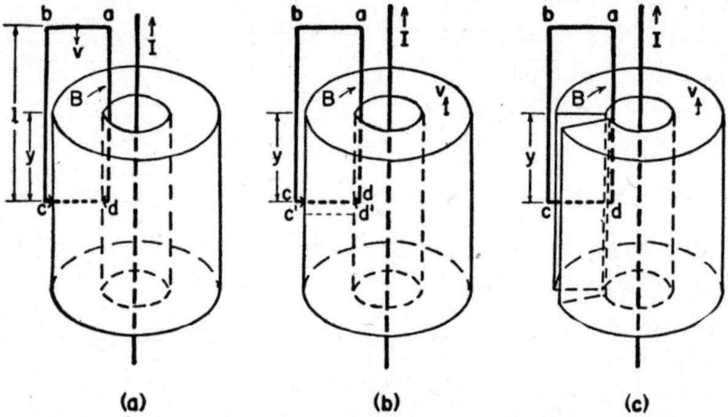

(a)   **(b)**   **(c)**

Figure 33. Concentric Iron Cylinder Surrounding a Wire.

The total rate of change of flux linkages is

$$\frac{d(N\phi)}{dt} = \left(\mu \frac{dy}{dt} - \frac{dy}{dt}\right)0.2I \log \frac{r_2}{r_1}$$

$$= v(\mu - 1)0.2I \log \frac{r_2}{r_1}$$

$$= -e_v - e_m + \phi \frac{dN}{dt}$$

The increase of flux linkages due to the cutting action of the instantaneous conducting line cd is just balanced by the decrease of flux linkages due to the substitution of circuit $c'd'$ for cd.

(E) The total voltage is

$$e = e_v + e_m = v0.2I \log \frac{r_2}{r_1}$$

or the same as for *Case a*.

Case c

Finally, in Fig. 33(c), suppose a thin axial slot to be cut through the cylinder so that it can slip by a rigid circuit *abcd*. Then

(A) Select axes (x,y,z).

(B) The flux inside the circuit is changing by the amount contributed by the iron, hence the variational component of voltage is

$$e_v = -\frac{\partial \phi}{\partial t} = -\frac{\partial}{\partial t} y \int_{r_1}^{r_2} B_i \, dr = -v(\mu - 1)0.2I \log \frac{r_2}{r_1}$$

(C) The circuit itself is stationary, so there is no motional component of voltage.

(D) The circuit is unbroken, so there can be no substitution of circuit. The rate of change of flux linkages is

$$\frac{d(N\phi)}{dt} = \left(\mu \frac{dy}{dt} - \frac{dy}{dt}\right)0.2I \log \frac{r_2}{r_1}$$

$$= v(\mu - 1)0.2I \log \frac{r_2}{r_1}$$

$$= -e_v$$

or due entirely to transformer action.

(E) The total voltage is

$$e = e_v$$

The above three cases can be summarized as follows (putting $C = v0.2 \log r_2/r_1$):

Fig.	$\partial \phi/\partial t$	$\oint B \times V \cdot ds$	$N \, d\phi/dt$	$\phi \, dN/dt$	$d(N\phi)/dt$
33(a)	0	$-C$	$-C$	μC	$(\mu - 1)C$
33(b)	$(\mu - 1)C$	$-\mu C$	$-C$	μC	$(\mu - 1)C$
33(c)	$(\mu - 1)C$	0	$(\mu - 1)C$	0	$(\mu - 1)C$

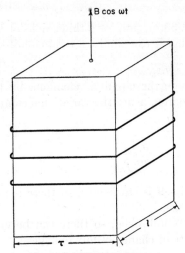

Figure 34. The Transformer.

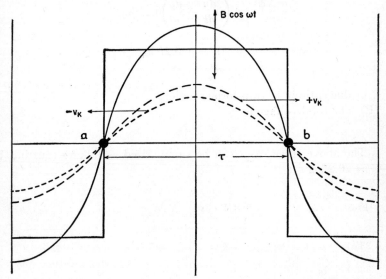

Figure 35. Resolution of Standing Wave into Pair of Traveling Waves.

Thus in each case the total rate of change of flux linkages is the same, but the total voltage induced is not the same for the last case as for the first two cases, nor are these voltages divided in the same way between variational and motional components. The arbitrary choice of reference axis (moving circuit or moving cylinder) is seen to change the interpretation, while the elimination of a substitution of circuit (*Case c*) introduces a considerable change.

THE TRANSFORMER

Consider an ideal transformer, Fig. 34, having a rectangular core of section τl, and ignore the leakage flux. Then at any instant the flux density is uniform over the core, and the equation of its time and space distribution in the direction of τ may be taken as that of a rectangular standing wave

$$B(x,t) = \frac{4}{\pi}\sum_{k=1}^{\infty} \frac{B}{2k-1} \sin (2k-1)\frac{\pi x}{\tau} \cos \omega t$$

and the flux in the core is

$$\phi(t) = l\int_0^\tau B(x,t)\,dx = \tau l B\frac{8}{\pi^2}\sum_1^\infty \frac{\cos \omega t}{(2k-1)^2} = \Phi \cos \omega t$$

since
$$\tau l B = \Phi$$

and
$$\frac{8}{\pi^2}\sum_1^\infty \frac{1}{(2k-1)^2} = 1$$

The transformer is a pure case of variational voltage, so

$$e = e_v = -N\frac{\partial \phi}{\partial t} = \omega N\Phi \sin \omega t$$

However, the standing wave of flux density may be expressed as a pair of equal traveling waves moving in opposite directions, thus

$$B(x,t) = \frac{2}{\pi} \sum_1^\infty \frac{B}{(2k-1)} \left\{ \sin \left[\frac{(2k-1)\pi x}{\tau} - \omega t \right] \right.$$

$$+ \sin \left[\frac{(2k-1)\pi x}{\tau} + \omega t \right] \left. \right\}$$

$$= \Sigma \beta' + \Sigma \beta''$$

in which the velocity of a harmonic wave is

$$v_k = \frac{\omega \tau}{(2k-1)\pi}$$

and its magnitude is $2B/(2k-1)\pi$.

The fundamental components of these traveling waves are indicated in Fig. 35 by dotted lines, while the standing wave is shown by full lines.

Now it is perfectly possible to calculate the voltage of the transformer as due entirely to *cutting action*, if we deal with the traveling waves and employ the principle of superposition. The forward waves $\Sigma \beta'$ moving to the right cut conductor a at $x = 0$ and cut conductor b at $x = \tau$. Likewise the backward waves $\Sigma \beta''$ moving to the left cut these conductors. The total voltage induced in the coil of which a and b are the coil sides then is

$$e = e_m$$

$$= -Nl\Sigma(\beta'_{x=0} - \beta'_{x=\tau} - \beta''_{x=0} + \beta''_{x=\tau})v_k$$

$$= -\omega Nl\tau B \frac{2}{\pi^2} \sum_1^\infty \frac{1}{(2k-1)^2} \{ \sin [-\omega t] - \sin [(2k-1)\pi - \omega t]$$

$$- \sin [+\omega t] + \sin [(2k-1)\pi + \omega t] \}$$

$$= \omega Nl\tau B \frac{8}{\pi^2} \sum_1^\infty \frac{1}{(2k-1)^2} \sin \omega t = \omega N\Phi \sin \omega t$$

the same as calculated by the variational method.

Although the correct result has been obtained by decomposing the standing wave into harmonic traveling waves and then computing the induced voltage as due to "cutting action," yet at the conductors themselves the flux density is zero, for

$$\Sigma\beta'_{x=0} + \Sigma\beta''_{x=0} = \frac{2}{\pi}\sum_1^\infty \frac{B}{(2k-1)}\{\sin[-\omega t] + \sin[+\omega t]\} = 0$$

$$\Sigma\beta'_{x=\tau} + \Sigma\beta''_{x=\tau} = \frac{2}{\pi}\sum_1^\infty \frac{B}{(2k-1)}\{\sin[(2k-1)\pi - \omega t]$$
$$+ \sin[(2k-1)\pi + \omega t]\} = 0$$

Thus in reality there is no resultant flux density at the conductors, and therefore the calculation of the induced voltage as due to cutting action is something of a subterfuge.

MOVING BAR

Figure 36 shows a bar ab moving at velocity v along rails $a'a$ and $b'b$ through a constant uniform field of density B. An external part $cdef$ completes the circuit. Taking reference axes on the external circuit, it is obvious that this is a simple case of cutting action and the voltage is

$$e = e_m = -Blv$$

The negative rate of change of flux is also

$$-\frac{d\phi}{dt} = -Blv$$

There is no substitution of circuit as long as the bar is on the *same* side of the external circuit $cdef$, but if the bar passes under this external circuit a substitution of circuit occurs, for circuit $abcdefa$ is a different circuit from $a'b'cdefa'$. The flux linkages of the former are increasing, while those of the latter are decreasing. A whole succession of moving bars could be added, so that instead of a single bar ab we would have a moving ladder of many rungs, all rungs in parallel and experiencing the same induced voltage. Ultimately, as the number of rungs is increased, and the spacing between them reduced, we come to a *continuous moving strip* of metal, Fig. 37.

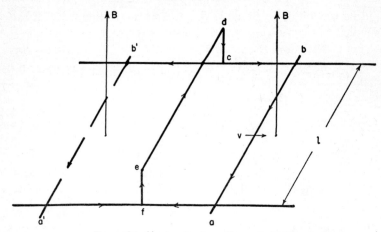

Figure 36. Moving Bar in a Magnetic Field.

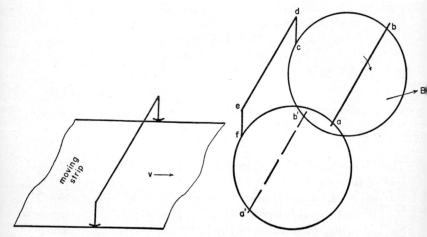

Figure 37. Moving Strip.   Figure 38. Rotating Bar in a Radial Field.

But take the reference axes on the conductor ab. The flux density is still constant everywhere with respect to the reference frame, so $\partial\phi/\partial t = 0$ and there is no variational component of voltage. It is now the lead ed which is moving backward at velocity v through the flux density B, causing a voltage

$$e = e_m = -Blv$$

the same as before.

Let us now bend the guide rails $a'a$ and $b'b$ into circles, the flux density B between them being constant as before but directed radially outwards as shown in Fig. 38. Then as bar ab revolves it cuts through the flux inducing a d-c voltage

$$e = -Blv$$

and the flux linked with the circuit $abcdefa$ steadily increases until the bar ab passes under leads fc. Then the flux linkages are reduced to zero and must start building up again on the *new* circuit. Thus a substitution of circuit is accomplished automatically each time bar ab passes under the external circuit. It is as though in Fig. 36 we threw the bar ab away when it reached the end of the rails and started out again with an entirely new bar $a'b'$ at the start of the rails. Figure 38 is, of course, the homopolar generator of Fig. 20.

MOVING CONDUCTOR WITH A CONCENTRIC IRON CYLINDER

Figure 39(a) shows a copper bar mn inside a hollow iron cylinder f moving at velocity v on rails ab and cd through a field of constant flux density B (that is, constant before being disturbed by the iron cylinder f). What is the magnitude and nature of the voltage induced in the closed circuit $mncb$?

Figure 39(b) shows an end view of the copper conductor m inside the iron cylinder f, and flux lines $1, 2, \cdots, 8$ of the field B. Consider the motion to take place in two stages: First, the iron cylinder is moved over one flux line, as indicated in Fig. 39(c), and second, the copper conductor is then moved to the proper position in the center cf the cylinder, as indicated in Fig. 39(d). Obviously, the movement of the iron cylinder reduces the flux linked with the circuit by flux line 5, which is transferred from the left to the right side of the cylinder. For a uniform movement of the cylinder the rate of flux transfer is

$$\frac{\partial \phi}{\partial t} = -Blv$$

and this will induce in the closed circuit a *variational* component of voltage

$$e_v = -\frac{\partial \phi}{\partial t} = Blv$$

Now when the copper conductor *mn* is moved from its position in *b* or *c* to its position in *d*, it cuts through zero flux density, since

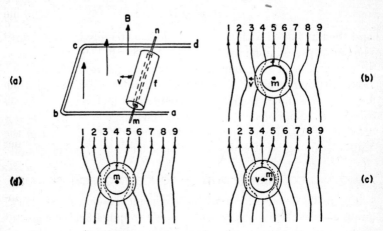

Figure 39. Moving Conductor with Iron Cylinder.

all the flux passes through the walls of the iron cylinder, and therefore there is no *motional* component of induced voltage,

$$e_m = 0$$

If, now, iron cylinder and copper conductor move simultaneously at the same uniform velocity it is perfectly clear that the induced voltage is due entirely to the *variational* component brought about by the transfer of flux through the cylinder, and there is, in fact, no motional component of voltage whatever induced. Superficially, of course, it appears that the voltage is due to "cutting action," especially since it is given numerically by $e = Blv$; but, as we have seen, the action is in reality transformer induction. However, since the correct result is obtained by the Blv rule, this may be called a case of *quasi-motional emf.* The voltage of a d-c generator induced in the coils embedded in its armature slots is of this nature; for the copper conductors do not "cut" the flux at all—the flux through the teeth on either side of the coil slot merely transfers from one side to the other and *the true cause of the induction is transformer*

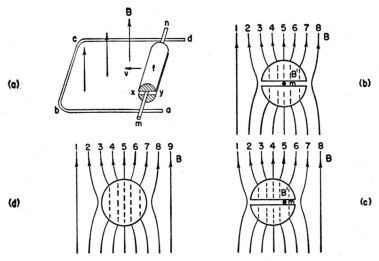

Figure 40. Solid Iron Cylinder Moving through a Uniform Field.

action! Thus one of the oldest and most cherished examples of cutting action goes into the discard. It is likely, however, that professors will continue to teach, and engineers to believe, for many years to come, that the *Blv* rule is perfectly proper when applied to a d-c generator. And it is! But not for the reasons they think.

SOLID IRON CYLINDER MOVING THROUGH A UNIFORM FIELD

In Fig. 40(a) is shown a conductor *mn* in a thin slot *xy* of an iron cylinder *f*. Conductor and cylinder are moving at velocity *v* along rails *ab* and *cd* of a closed circuit *mncb* through a flux of constant density *B* (that is, constant until disturbed by the iron cylinder). What is the nature and magnitude of the induced voltage?

In Fig. 40(b) the flux lines 1, 2, $\cdots$, 8 are indicated as concentrated on the iron cylinder, and the vertical component of flux density inside the iron near its center is B'. Of course, $B' > B$ and the flux density in the thin slot is also B'.

Suppose the movement to be made in two stages: First, the iron cylinder moves to the left one flux line, and then conductor m is moved over to its center position. During the movement of the iron cylinder by an amount Δx the flux inside the circuit $mncb$ is increased by an amount

$$\Delta\phi = (B' - B)l\Delta x$$

thereby inducing a *variational* component of voltage

$$e_v = -\frac{\Delta\phi}{\Delta t} = -(B' - B)l\frac{\Delta x}{\Delta t} = -(B' - B)lv$$

Now let conductor mn be moved to the left, Fig. 40(c), by amount Δx so as to bring it back to its center position. During this movement it is cutting through flux density B', decreasing the flux inside circuit $mncb$, and thereby inducing a *motional* component of voltage

$$e_m = +B'lv$$

But if the iron cylinder and conductor mn move simultaneously at uniform velocity v, the total voltage induced in the circuit becomes

$$e = e_v + e_m = -(B' - B)lv + B'lv = Blv$$

and this is exactly the same voltage as would be generated by the movement of the conductor mn through the uniform field B.

This case differs from the previous example of a conductor inside a hollow iron cylinder in that *both* variational and motional components of voltage are present. Strangely enough, however, the resultant voltage comes from the variational and not the motional term.

It is now but a step to fill in the thin slot, Fig. 40(d), and consider the conductor to be any filament of the iron cylinder, and so we see that the induced voltage is the *quasi-motional emf*

$$e = Blv$$

The reader is warned, that in applying the General Criteria to cases of this type, where the space flux distribution itself depends on the motion, that the motion cannot be stopped in determining the variational component of voltage. We must allow the motion responsible for the variation of flux to proceed, but consider the *circuit* to remain stationary while computing the variational component of voltage.

CHAPTER VII

THEOREM of CONSTANT FLUX LINKAGES

The general method of attacking a problem on the transients of electrical circuits or machines consists in setting up the differential equation and solving it in conformity with the given terminal (initial and final) and boundary conditions. The solution is always in two parts:

1. The *particular integral*, depending on the form of the applied voltage, and representing the final *steady-state* solution.
2. The *complementary solution*, independent of the applied voltage but depending on the initial conditions (charges, currents, flux linkages, etc.), and representing the *transient* from the initial to the final conditions.

We may therefore write

$$\left\{ \begin{array}{c} \text{Complete} \\ \text{solution} \end{array} \right\} = \left\{ \begin{array}{c} \text{Final} \\ \text{condition} \end{array} \right\} + \left\{ \text{Transient} \right\} \qquad (64)$$

Furthermore, since the complete solution at $t = 0$ must be the initial condition, we have

$$\left\{ \begin{array}{c} \text{Initial} \\ \text{condition} \end{array} \right\} = \left\{ \begin{array}{c} \text{Final} \\ \text{condition} \end{array} \right\} + \left\{ \begin{array}{c} \text{Transient terms} \\ \text{at } t = 0 \end{array} \right\} \qquad (65)$$

so that the magnitude of a transient may be estimated as the difference between the initial and final states. For example, if a weight suspended by a spring having a final position x_1 is pulled down to an initial position x_2 and then released, the resulting oscillation will have an amplitude of $A = (x_2 - x_1)$.

Now in many problems, particularly in those concerning short circuits in electrical machinery, it is either impossible or exceedingly difficult to obtain the complete transient solution. The final steady-state solution usually presents no difficulties. If a ready means were at hand for determining the initial conditions, and if the nature of the energy losses were known, Eq. (65) then might furnish a reasonable approximation to the desired solution. It so happens that in many practical cases these means are adequately provided by the *theorem of constant flux linkages* and a general knowledge of the way in which transients decay exponentially. This theorem was first formulated and extensively applied by R. E. Doherty[*] and has become an essential tool in the study of machine transients.

Consider a circuit j having a resistance r_j, self-inductance L_{jj}, and mutual inductances M_{jk} with neighboring circuits. Then the total flux linkages of this circuit are

$$\Omega_j = \Sigma N_j \phi_j = L_{jj} i_j + \Sigma M_{jk} i_k \qquad (66)$$

in which both the L_{jj} and M_{jk} may be functions of some parameter (position, angle, time, etc.). The differential equation for the circuit is

$$e_j = r_j i_j + \frac{d\Omega_j}{dt} = r_j i_j + \frac{d}{dt}(L_{jj} i_j + \Sigma M_{jk} i_k) \qquad (67)$$

Integrating over the interval $(t - t_0)$ and rearranging this gives

$$\Omega_j(t) - \Omega_j(t_0) = \int_{t_0}^{t} (e_j - r_j i_j)\, dt \qquad (68)$$

in which $\Omega_j(t_0)$ is the initial value of the flux linkages at $t = t_0$.

If the applied voltage is zero and the resistance of the circuit is negligible, there results

[*] "A Simplified Method of Analyzing Short-Circuit Problems" by R. E. Doherty, *Trans. A.I.E.E.*, vol. 42, 1923.

$$\Omega_j(t) = \Omega_j(0) = constant \text{ for } e_j = 0, r_j = 0 \qquad (69)$$

hence the flux linkages remain constant, that is,

$$L_{jj}i_j + \Sigma M_{jk}i_k = constant \qquad (70)$$

This equation shows that the currents will vary if the inductances change, but in such a way as to maintain constant flux linkages in the circuit. The practical significance of this deduction lies in the fact that the characteristics of the beginning part of a transient may be calculated on the assumptions of constant flux linkages, if it is known that the right-hand side of Eq. (68) is of little consequence over the time interval considered.

The theorem of constant flux linkages, corresponding to Eq. (69) or (70), may be stated in the following form:

> *The flux linkages of a closed circuit of zero resistance and zero applied voltage remain constant regardless of the way in which the self and mutual inductances may change, or the way in which the currents may vary.*

A further refinement is introduced in those cases where the applied voltage is held constant (for example, the exciter voltage on the field of a synchronous machine), for then

$$\int_{t_0}^{t} e_j \, dt = E_j(t - t_0) \qquad (71)$$

In the case of rotating machines it is known that the current in an armature or field circuit may consist of both a d-c and an a-c component, thus

$$i_j = I_j\epsilon^{-a_jt} + I_j'\epsilon^{-a_j't} \sin(\omega t + \phi) \qquad (72)$$

and that the exponential decrement factors cause these components to die out very slowly compared with the period of the a-c component. Then over each period $T = 1/f = 2\pi/\omega$ of the oscillation we have

$$\int_{t_0}^{t_0+T} I_j'\epsilon^{-a_j't} \sin(\omega t + \phi)dt \cong 0 \qquad (73)$$

$$\int_{t_0}^{t_0+T} I_j \epsilon^{-a_i t} \, dt = \frac{I_j}{a_j} \epsilon^{-a_i t_0}(1 - \epsilon^{-a_i T}) = \frac{I_j}{a_j} \epsilon^{-a_i t_0}\left(a_j T - \frac{a_j^2 T^2}{2} - \cdots\right)$$

$$\cong \frac{I_j}{a_j} \epsilon^{-a_i t_0} a_j T = I_j T \epsilon^{-a_i t_0} \tag{74}$$

Hereby Eq. (68) may be written

$$\Omega_j(t_0 + T) - \Omega_j(t_0) = (E_j - r_j I_j \epsilon^{-a_i t_0}) T \tag{75}$$

The procedure in applying this equation then is

1. Put $t_0 = 0$ and from $\Omega_j(t) = \Omega_j(0)$ determine the natural period of oscillation T and the initial current, of which the d-c component of circuit j is $I_j \epsilon^{-a_i T}$.
2. Put $t_0 = T$ and using the above value of $I_j \epsilon^{-a_i T}$ compute the current at $t = t_0 + T = 2T$ from Eq. (75), of which the new d-c component is $I_j \epsilon^{-a_i 2T}$.
3. Put $t_0 = 2T$ and using the above value of $I_j \epsilon^{-a_i 2T}$ compute the current at $t = 3T$ from Eq. (75), of which the new d-c component is $I_j \epsilon^{-a_i 3T}$. Continue in this fashion as far as required.

This procedure represents an extension of the original theorem, Eq. (69) or (70), as given by Doherty, and enables us to estimate the decrement of the currents when it is known that these decrements are not great over a time interval equal to the natural period of oscillation. But the procedure is not rigorous, for it ignores the effect on the decrement of the resistances of the neighboring circuits mutually coupled with the circuit under consideration.

It is important to note that the theorem of flux linkages applies only to *closed circuits*. If a circuit is first opened it can be maneuvered into some other position and then closed on quite different flux linkages from those it possessed before being opened. Or it can be opened in position and closed at some subsequent instant after the flux through it has changed. This is, in effect, a *substitution of circuit* and constitutes an exception to the theorem of constant flux linkages, just as it did in electromagnetic induction. Therefore,

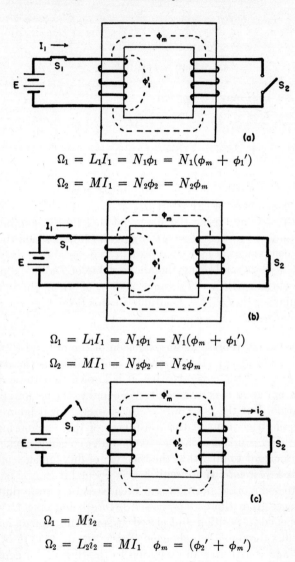

$$\Omega_1 = L_1 I_1 = N_1\phi_1 = N_1(\phi_m + \phi_1')$$
$$\Omega_2 = MI_1 = N_2\phi_2 = N_2\phi_m$$

$$\Omega_1 = L_1 I_1 = N_1\phi_1 = N_1(\phi_m + \phi_1')$$
$$\Omega_2 = MI_1 = N_2\phi_2 = N_2\phi_m$$

$$\Omega_1 = Mi_2$$
$$\Omega_2 = L_2 i_2 = MI_1 \quad \phi_m = (\phi_2' + \phi_m')$$

Figure 41. The Transformer.

*Flux linkages can be changed at will by a suitable
substitution of circuit, and the theorem of constant
flux linkages does not apply in such cases.*

However, a situation which constitutes a substitution of circuit
with respect to electromagnetic induction does not necessarily com-
prise a substitution of circuit with respect to the theorem of constant flux linkages. For example, the winding on of turns, Figs. 8
and 21, is a substitution of circuit as far as electromagnetic induction is concerned, but the theorem of constant flux linkages nevertheless applies to this case.

THE TRANSFORMER*

Figure 41(a) shows a two-winding transformer with the primary
connected to a battery, or constant voltage source, and the secondary open. The primary current $I_1 = E/r_1$ will establish a mutual
flux ϕ_m in the iron core linking both the primary and the secondary
windings, and a leakage flux ϕ_1' linking with the primary winding
only.

The flux linkages of the two windings under this condition (switch
S_1 closed, switch S_2 open) are

$$\Omega_1 = L_1 I_1 = N_1 \phi_1 = N_1(\phi_m + \phi_1')$$

$$\Omega_2 = M I_1 = N_2 \phi_2 = N_2 \phi_m$$

Closing switch S_2, Fig. 41(b), will have no effect on the fluxes **or**
the currents.

Let switch S_1 be opened, interrupting the primary circuit $i_1 = 0$.
According to the theorem of constant flux linkages the flux linkages
Ω_2 cannot change in the first instant, and if the secondary resistance
is neglected Ω_2 must remain constant indefinitely, that is, a secondary current i_2 must appear such as will satisfy the relationship

$$\Omega_2 = L_2 i_2 = M I_1 = constant \text{ or } i_2 = \frac{M}{L_2} I_1$$

Now suppose the secondary winding to be removed from the

* "A Simplified Method of Analyzing Short-Circuit Problems" by R. E.
Doherty, *Trans. A.I.E.E.*, vol. 42, 1923.

core, as shown in Fig. 42. The secondary inductance L_2' is then much reduced,

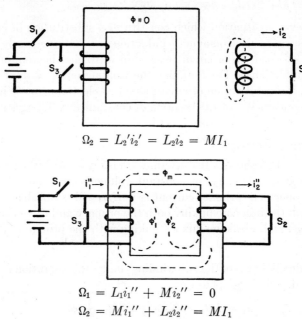

$$\Omega_2 = L_2'i_2' = L_2i_2 = MI_1$$

$$\Omega_1 = L_1i_1'' + Mi_2'' = 0$$
$$\Omega_2 = Mi_1'' + L_2i_2'' = MI_1$$

Figure 42. Removing and Replacing the Secondary.

but its flux linkages must remain constant,

$$\Omega_2 = L_2'i_2' = L_2i_2 = MI_1 = constant$$

The current in the secondary then increases some 200-fold: $i_2' = I_1M/L_2'$.

The work done in withdrawing the secondary winding is equal to the difference in stored magnetic energy between its final and initial positions,

$$W = \tfrac{1}{2}L_2'i_2'^2 - \tfrac{1}{2}L_2i_2^2 = \tfrac{1}{2}L_2'\left(\frac{M}{L_2'}I_1\right)^2 - \tfrac{1}{2}L_2\left(\frac{M}{L_2}I_1\right)^2$$

$$= \frac{M^2I_1^2}{2}\frac{L_2 - L_2'}{L_2L_2'}$$

Next, let switch S_3 be closed (there is no flux in the core at this instant), and then replace the secondary winding on the core. The flux linkages remain constant, so that

$$\Omega_1 = L_1 i_1'' + M i_2'' = 0$$

$$\Omega_2 = M i_1'' + L_2 i_2'' = M I_1$$

and solving these simultaneous equations, there results

$$i_1'' = \frac{-M^2 I_1}{L_1 L_2 - M^2}$$

$$i_2'' = \frac{L_1 M I_1}{L_1 L_2 - M^2}$$

Thus it is seen that the currents may vary considerably as switches are opened and closed and the positions of circuits changed, but the flux linkages of closed circuits remain invariant. Note, however, that the opening and closing of a circuit permits its flux linkages to be changed as desired, and the theorem of constant flux linkages is inapplicable under such conditions (substitution of circuits).

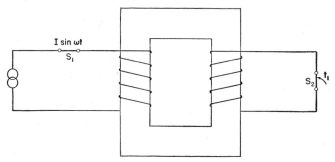

Figure 43. Short-Circuiting the Secondary.

Figure 43 shows a transformer with an a-c voltage applied. Before switch S_2 is closed the flux linkages are

$$\Omega_1 = L_1 I_1 \sin \omega t$$

$$\Omega_2 = M I_1 \sin \omega t$$

Let switch S_2 of the secondary be closed at $t = t_1$. The primary flux linkages must continue to vary sinusoidally, since the applied voltage is maintained as

$$E_1 \cos \omega t = \frac{d\Omega_1}{dt} = \omega L_1 I_1 \cos \omega t$$

But the primary and secondary currents must change so as to maintain constant flux linkages in the secondary. Hence

$$\Omega_1 = L_1 i_1 + M i_2 = L_1 I_1 \sin \omega t$$

$$\Omega_2 = M i_1 + L_2 i_2 = M I_1 \sin \omega t_1$$

from which

$$i_1 = \frac{L_1 L_2 \sin \omega t - M^2 \sin \omega t_1}{L_1 L_2 - M^2} I_1$$

$$i_2 = \frac{\sin \omega t_1 - \sin \omega t}{L_1 L_2 - M^2} I_1 L_1 M$$

Thus the currents contain d-c components,

$$I_{1(1)} = \frac{-M^2 I_1 \sin \omega t_1}{L_1 L_2 - M^2}$$

$$I_{2(1)} = \frac{L_1 M I_1 \sin \omega t_1}{L_1 L_2 - M^2}$$

and a-c components

$$i_{1(ac)} = \frac{L_1 L_2}{L_1 L_2 - M^2} I_1 \sin \omega t$$

$$i_{2(ac)} = \frac{-L_1 M}{L_1 L_2 - M^2} I_1 \sin \omega t$$

But the a-c components are also the steady-state solutions (neglecting resistance). Hence by Eqs. (64) and (65) the d-c components are the initial values of the transient terms, which may be expected to die out. Considering only the d-c components, the differential equations of the circuit are

$$L_1\frac{di_1}{dt} + M\frac{di_2}{dt} = -r_1i_1$$

$$M\frac{di_1}{dt} + L_2\frac{di_2}{dt} = -r_2i_2$$

Eliminating either i_1 or i_2 from this pair of equations and rearranging, there results the differential equation

$$\frac{di}{dt} + \frac{r_2L_1 + r_1L_2}{L_1L_2 - M^2}i = 0$$

the solution to which is

$$i = I\epsilon^{-at} \qquad a = \frac{r_2L_1 + r_1L_2}{L_1L_2 - M^2}$$

Substituting the initial values for these d-c currents previously obtained, there results

$$i_{1(dc)} = \frac{-M^2}{L_1L_2 - M^2}I_1 \sin \omega t_1 \epsilon^{-at}$$

$$i_{2(dc)} = \frac{L_1M}{L_1L_2 - M^2}I_1 \sin \omega t_1 \epsilon^{-at}$$

The complete solutions then are, approximately,

$$i_1 = i_{1(ac)} + i_{1(dc)} = \frac{I_1}{L_1L_2 - M^2}(L_1L_2 \sin \omega t - M^2\epsilon^{-at} \sin \omega t_1)$$

$$i_2 = i_{2(ac)} + i_{2(dc)} = \frac{I_1L_1M}{L_1L_2 - M^2}(-\sin \omega t + \epsilon^{-at} \sin \omega t_1)$$

It is of interest to estimate the decrement by the method of Eq. (75). Let t_k be any instant, and $T = 1/f = 2\pi/\omega$ the time of one cycle. Then

$$\frac{d\Omega_1}{dt} = E_1 \cos \omega t - r_1i_1$$

$$\frac{d\Omega_2}{dt} = 0 - r_2i_2$$

Integrating these equations over a period T, (and assuming that the integrals of alternating components, with or without decrements, are substantially zero over this range) there results

$$\Omega_1(t_k + T) - \Omega(t_k) = \int_{t_k}^{t_k+T} (E_1 \cos \omega t - r_1 i_1) dt = -r_1 T I_1(t_k)$$

$$\Omega_2(t_k + T) - \Omega_2(t_k) = \int_{t_k}^{t_k+T} (-r_2 i_2) dt = -r_2 T I_2(t_k)$$

in which $I_1(t_k) = $ d-c component of current in circuit 1 at time t_k

$I_2(t_k) = $ d-c component of current in circuit 2 at time t_k

The *changes* in flux linkages over the cycle of period T then are

$$\Delta\Omega_1(t_k) = -r_1 T I_1(t_k)$$

$$\Delta\Omega_2(t_k) = -r_2 T I_2(t_k)$$

Therefore, the flux linkage equations for any instant t in the interval $t_k \leq t \leq (t_k + T)$ become

$$\Omega_1(t) = L_1 i_1 + M i_2 = L_1 I_1 \sin \omega t - r_1 T \Sigma I_1(t_k)$$

$$\Omega_2(t) = M i_1 + L_2 i_2 = M I_1 \sin \omega t_1 - r_2 T \Sigma I_2(t_k)$$

in which the $r T \Sigma I(t_k)$ are to include all the changes in flux linkages up to the beginning of the particular period T under consideration, as indicated in Fig. 44.

Solving these equations for the instantaneous currents we obtain

$$i_1 = I_1 \frac{L_1 L_2 \sin \omega t - M^2 \sin \omega t_1}{L_1 L_2 - M^2} - \frac{r_1 L_2 T \Sigma I_{1(\mathrm{dc})}(t_k) - r_2 M T \Sigma I_{2(\mathrm{dc})}(t_k)}{L_1 L_2 - M^2}$$

$$i_2 = I_1 \frac{L_1 M(-\sin \omega t + \sin \omega t_1)}{L_1 L_2 - M^2} + \frac{r_1 M T \Sigma I_{1(\mathrm{dc})}(t_k) - r_2 L_1 T \Sigma I_{2(\mathrm{dc})}(t_k)}{L_1 L_2 - M^2}$$

The second terms on the right are responsible for the decrement in the flux linkages and currents.

The procedure in applying these equations is then as follows:

1. For the initial period beginning at the instant of short-circuit, t_1, and lasting until $t_2 = t_1 + T$, ignore the resistance terms in the equations for i_1 and i_2.

2. For the next period $t_2 = t_1 + T$ to $t_3 = t_1 + 2T$, the d-c components are taken as

$$I_1(t_2) = -\frac{M^2 \sin \omega t_1}{L_1 L_2 - M^2} I_1$$

$$I_2(t_2) = -\frac{L_1 M \sin \omega t_1}{L_1 L_2 - M^2} I_1$$

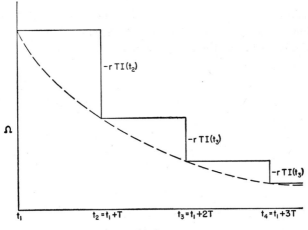

Figure 44. Decrement.

and the constant flux linkages for this period are decreased by $r_1 T I_1(t_2)$ and $r_2 T I_2(t_2)$ from the values used in the previous period; that is, these terms are used in the right-hand side of the equations for i_1 and i_2.

3. For the next period $t_3 = t_1 + 2T$ to $t_4 = t_1 + 3T$, the d-c components are taken as

$$I_1(t_3) = \frac{-I_1 M^2 \sin \omega t_1 - r_1 L_2 T I_1(t_2) + r_2 M T I_2(t_2)}{L_1 L_2 - M^2}$$

$$I_2(t_3) = \frac{I_1 L_1 M \sin \omega t_1 + r_1 M T I_1(t_2) - r_2 L_1 T I_2(t_2)}{L_1 L_2 - M^2}$$

and the constant flux linkages for this period are decreased by $r_1 T I_1(t_3)$ and $r_2 T I_2(t_3)$ from the values used in the previous equations; that is, these terms are included in the right-hand side of the equations for i_1 and i_2.

4. Proceeding in this way—determining the d-c components of current at the end of each period and decreasing the constant flux linkages for the next period by proportional amounts— the decrement can be approximated.

Of course, in this simple example, no purpose is served by approximating the decrements by the above procedure, but in more complicated cases the method may have merit.

INDEX

Basic laws, interrelationship, 2

Circuit, 2, 9
    definition, 4, 8
    direction, 4–8
    folding, 5–8
    knotting, 5–8
    substitution of, 3, 12
    turning, 5–8
    twisting, 5–8
Commutation, 18
Concentric iron cylinder surrounding a wire, 71–75
Constant flux linkage theorem, 86–88
Coordinate system, 26, 27, 31, 40
Criteria, 3, 39, 40
Cutting action, 3, 15, 25, 26, 38

D-C
    generator, 23, 25, 38, 47, 49
    voltage, 21–23, 40, 42, 43

Electromagnetic induction, 20, 31, 40

Faraday disk, 62–68
Faraday's law of electromagnetic induction, 1, 2, 3, 20, 39, 42
Flux, 9, 28
    density, 9, 27

Flux linkages, 10, 15, 18, 20, 39, 42, 86
    rate of change, 20

General solution, 27–33
Gradient, voltage
    motional, 41
    total, 34, 66
    variational, 40, 67

Heaviside's second circuital relationship, 34, 42, 70
Homopolar generator, 47, 81

Motional component of voltage, 25, 26, 31, 38
Moving bar, 78–81
Moving coil, 23–26, 27, 45
Moving conductor with concentric iron cylinder, 81
Moving strip, 79, 80
Multiple-spoke wheel, 57

Oscillating bar generator, 51

Paradoxes, 44

Single-spoke wheel, 55
Sliding contact, 13–15, 18, 46
Solid iron cylinder moving through a uniform field, 83

Stationary (fixed) coil, 44
Substitution of circuit, 3, 12–19, 41, 42, 43
    commutation, 18, 58, 63
    definition, 12
    sliding contact, 13–15, 18
    tap changing, 17
    winding on of turns, 15–18
    with respect to the theorem of
      constant flux linkages, 89–90
Swinging bar generator, 52

Tap changing, 17
Theorem of constant flux linkages, 86, 88
Transformer, 77–79, 91–98
    action, 3, 25, 31, 38, 40, 42, 44, 45
Turns, 3, 8–11
    definition, 11, 16
    winding on of, 15–18

Universal generator, 59

Variational component of voltage, 25, 26, 31, 38
Vector potential, 28, 66–68
Voltage
    cutting action, 3, 15, 25, 31, 38, 41
    d-c component, 21–23
    in element of a circuit, 33
    machines, 35
    motional component, 25, 31, 38, 41
    total, 25, 31, 32
    transformer action, 3, 25, 26, 31, 38, 40
    variational component, 25, 26, 31, 38, 40

Winding on of turns, 15–18
Wire in zero magnetic field, 69